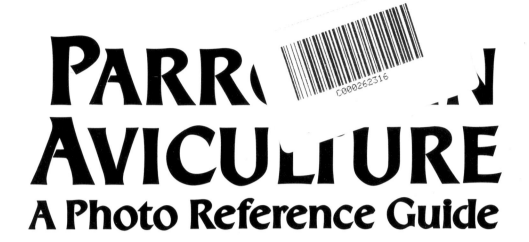

PARROTS IN AVICULTURE
A Photo Reference Guide

Rosemary Low

Photographs by
Ron and Val Moat

BLANDFORD

A BLANDFORD BOOK

First published in the UK 1992
by Blandford
(a Cassell imprint)
Villiers House
41/47 Strand
LONDON
WC2N 5JE

Distributed in Australia
by Capricorn Link (Australia) Pty Ltd
PO Box 665, Lane Cove, NSW 2066

British Library Cataloguing in Publication Data
Low, Rosemary
   Parrots in aviculture.
   I. Title
   636.6865

ISBN 0–7137–2279–7

Typeset in Monophoto Erhardt by
August Filmsetting, Haydock, St Helens

Printed and bound in Hong Kong by Dah Hua Printing Co.

This book is dedicated to Dr Peter Evans, whose skill, diplomacy, wisdom and, above all, untiring dedication to the conservation of the parrots of Dominica (the highly endangered Imperial and the endangered Red-necked) has set standards that will be hard to surpass for those conservation biologists destined to work with endangered parrots in the years to come.

Contents

Acknowledgements

I am most grateful to the following for complying so readily with my requests for information: Thomas Arndt, Germany; Vincent Guinnet, France; John Heath, UK; Dieter Hoppe, Germany; Ron Johnson, USA; Nelson Kawall, Brazil; Herman Kremer, Netherlands; Heinz Loelfing, Germany; G. A. Smith, UK; John and Geraldine Stevens, UK; and Roger Wilkinson, UK. And also to Klaus Paulmann for so kindly checking the German names used.

Photographs
I am indebted to my good friends Ron and Val Moat for the vast majority of the photographs (their work inspired this book) and to the owners of Loro Parque and Palmitos Park for permitting them to photograph the birds.

Additional photographs were taken by Walt Hansen (USA), page 266; Carlos Keller, Brazil (page 236); Gerhard Hofmann, Germany (page 55); Peter Odekerken, Australia (pages 37, 41, 45, 52, 53, 67, 85, 113, 114, 118, 128); R. H. Grantham, page 203; and the author (pages 54, 66, 93, 168, 193, 213, 271).

Preface

Whilst there have been a number of excellent books in several languages that have illustrated with photographs some of the parrot species known in aviculture, until now none has shown the vast majority of species. For a long time I have been aware of the need for such a book, one which uses good-quality photographs to depict as many as possible of the 220 or so species known in aviculture. Hence this volume.

Without the photographers Ron and Val Moat, together with the cooperation of the owners of Loro Parque and Palmitos Park in the Canary Islands – where all but 18 of the photographs were taken – and the help of Mike Gammond in catching the birds and placing them in the photo-cage, this book could not have existed.

The text is designed to be concise but informative and will appeal especially to those who need rapid access to the most pertinent information. It is also intended for use by people who have a basic command of English and are unable to obtain a book on parrots in their own language. Above all, it aims to provide instant identification of the species of parrots in aviculture.

Rosemary Low
Canary Islands, 1992

Introduction

Their dazzling colours, ability to mimic human speech and adaptability to captivity have made the parrots arguably the best-known group of birds in existence. Most parrot species are colourful, the principal exceptions being the cockatoos, which are mainly white or black, and the Vasas, which are entirely grey. The others, more than 300 species, display a wider range and combination of colours than any other avian group. Approximately 9,000 bird species exist today, of which about 3 per cent (about 330 species) are parrots. (Taxonomists differ concerning whether some should be classified as species or sub-species). After decades during which no new parrot species were named – and during which it was also generally assumed that all existing parrots were known – three 'new' species were discovered and named during the 1980s, two from Peru and one from Brazil. Who knows how many other species await discovery in tropical forests?

During the 1980s tropical forests became an issue of worldwide concern. The scale of their destruction threatened not only birds and other fauna but also millions of humans. As Christoph Imboden, director of the International Council for Bird Preservation, has pointed out:

> Flooding, soil erosion and only transient agricultural productivity have been the results of clearing the forests. The lives of an estimated 500 million people have been disrupted by such unnatural disasters, and the economic costs can be calculated in billions of dollars . . .
>
> Because of the unusually low density at which the great majority of birds inhabit tropical forests, and because of the often razor-sharp adaptations they have made, they can be extremely sensitive indicators of ecological change within the tropical forest biome.

This is especially true of parrots. Not until the 1980s were field studies of parrots, notably endangered and threatened species, carried out to a significant degree. By the end of the decade it was estimated that one-third of all parrot species were threatened with extinction. They highlighted the fact that, faced with loss or degradation of habitat and, in many cases, also with trapping for export or local trade, parrot populations can decline with extreme rapidity.

When this occurs, legislation against trade and deforestation is, by itself, useless in halting the decline. Without the help of conservationists, ornithologists, or experts in land use to educate local people in the importance of forest conservation and fauna protection, nothing can be achieved. But with the right persons performing this role, great success is possible. Especially on islands, endemic parrots can become the focus of eco-tourism, a source of local pride to be fiercely protected. The first example, and one which will surely pass into the annals of bird conservation, relates to the pioneering work of Paul Butler on St Lucia in the Caribbean. By involving a large percentage of the population, especially children, in its survival, the fortunes of the rapidly declining St Lucia Parrot (*Amazona versicolor*) were turned around in less than a decade. By 1990 its population had increased to 250, probably the maximum that the habitat can hold. A decade earlier only 150 survived in 39 sq. km (15 sq. miles).

At the same time, on the nearby island of Dominica the population of the magnificent Imperial Parrot (*Amazona imperialis*) had fallen to only 60 birds (from possibly 150 only 3 or 4 years before) after the island was hit by Hurricane David in 1979. In the previous year, research zoologist Dr Peter Evans commenced his study of the Imperial and the other endemic parrot of Dominica, the Red-necked Amazon (see page 273). By 1990 the Imperial population had increased to an estimated 80, land essential for its survival had been purchased and Peter Evans had carried out important work in connection with forest conservation and land use. In 1980 I was privileged to see the Imperial Parrot in the wild and can appreciate the importance of Dr Evans's work – and that of other dedicated conservation biologists.

They deserve the support of all those who care about the accelerating rate of bird extinction and, indeed, all those who are concerned about the future of this planet. Therefore, half the author's royalties from this book will be donated, via The World Parrot Trust, to further Dr Evans's work on Dominica.

How to Use This Book

Order of Species

Taxonomic order is used, so that if the reader wishes to compare photographs of, for example, all the lories, or read the information on this group of parrots, it is easily accessible. The order followed in almost every case is that used by Forshaw (1973, 1978 and 1989), because so many readers will already be familiar with this arrangement.

English Common Name

The most widely used name is given. In Australia some names are quite different to those used elsewhere, especially for native species. The Australian name is given in parentheses.

German Common Name

The most widely used name is given.

Dutch Common Name

There were no recognized names for some of the rarer species. I am indebted to Herman Kremer of Noordbergum, Netherlands, for compiling the index of Dutch names (with great care and after consulting the Genootschap Onze Taal, the society which promotes the correct use of the Dutch language).

Length

Measurements are from beak to tip of tail. There can be considerable variation in individuals of the same species, especially in those with a wide geographical range.

Weight

In most cases the weights are those of captive birds. There can be extreme variation in individuals, the weight being influenced by diet, housing, sex, sub-species and age. Where more than 10 or so birds were weighed, the highest and lowest weights were not taken into account if these differed markedly from the norm. Chick weights, with 5 or 6 exceptions, were of chicks hatched in the author's care.

Immatures

There can be considerable variation in immature plumage, even in young from the same nest, so descriptions should be taken only as a guide. (In many species adults also show considerable variation in plumage.) Note that for the sake of brevity, the periophthalmic skin, the area of bare skin *surrounding* the eye, is referred to as the eye skin.

For Australian parrakeets reference is made to the wing-stripe. This is the series of white (or yellow-white) marks on the underside of the outermost flight feathers. Together they form a band across the underside of the wing.

Origin

Provides brief details of the country or areas of origin.

Status

In many species there is little or no recent information.

Aviculture

Gives information on whether the species is common or rare and on its prolificacy in captivity.

Accommodation

To avoid repetition, each type of accommodation has been given a number. The meanings are as follows:

1   Aviary with well-drained floor (sloping concrete with outlet holes, or pebbles) or suspended cage over concrete base.

2   Aviary with well-drained floor, suspended over concrete base, or indoor cage 1.2 m (4 ft) long in room with tiled surround and floor.

3   Walk-in aviary, minimum length 2.1 m (7 ft) or indoor cage minimum length 1.8 m (6 ft).

4   Walk-in aviary, minimum length 3 m (10 ft).

4a   As 4, but 2 m (6 ft 8 in) or 2.5 m (8 ft 4 in) long.

5   Walk-in aviary, minimum length 4.5 m (13 ft 6 in).

6   Walk-in aviary, minimum length 7 m (21 ft).

7   Aviary or suspended cage, minimum length 2 m (6 ft 8 in).

8   Aviary or suspended cage, minimum length 3 m (10 ft).

9   Cage or aviary, indoors or outdoors, minimum length 1.2 m (4 ft).

10   Outdoor aviary, minimum length 1.5 m (5 ft) with enclosed shelter, for 1 or 2 pairs. Several pairs can be kept together and will breed, usually without problems, in a larger aviary. A planted aviary is ideal, provided that the plants can be cleaned easily.

11   Although this species is often kept and bred in a suspended cage only 3 m (10 ft) long, or even less, the quality of life and long-term well-being of such an intelligent bird must be considered. If a small cage is used for breeding, the birds should have access to a large enclosure, at least 15 m (50 ft) long, in which to fly for part of the year, as they will not fly in a small aviary. Keeping them permanently indoors, in a basement, for example, is not recommended.

11a   As 11, disregarding reference to 'often kept and bred'.

12   Aviary or suspended cage, minimum length 4 m (13 ft), or 3 m (10 ft) for breeding with access to longer flight for part of each year.

Diet

To avoid repetition, each type of diet has been given a number, the meaning of which is given below. Bear in mind that these are only suggestions, and that a number of factors influence the foods offered and eaten. No mention is made of pelleted foods because the author believes that the diet should be composed of a variety of items with, where appropriate, an emphasis on fresh fruits and vegetables.

1   Nectar (the name given to the liquid food offered to lories, which, of course, bears little resemblance to the nectar they would take from blossoms) – a proprietary type specially formulated for *small* species (*Charmosyna*, etc.) or a mixture of baby cereal (avoiding those containing lactose – milk sugar – if possible) and honey, and malt extract or molasses, mixed with water (preferably bottled water) – this should be made fresh once or twice daily; also apple, pear and, if available, cactus fruits.

2   Nectar – a proprietary type or made from the items described above, with the addition of wheat-germ cereal if desired; fresh fruit once or twice daily, especially apple, pear, orange, cactus fruits, grapes and bananas, but any fruit can be offered; and one or more of the following items daily: carrot, fresh raw corn on the cob or tinned sweet-corn, green leaves such as Swiss chard, spinach or lettuce, rearing food made from hard-boiled egg, wholegrain bread, low-fat cheese and carrot, ground up and mixed to a crumbly consistency.

3   Nectar – as in 2, and comprising at least 40 per cent of the diet, except for Iris and Musschenbroek's Lorikeets, which require only 5 or 10 per cent nectar; vegetables and fruit, as described in 2, plus dried figs soaked in water for a few hours, spray millet and a small amount of soaked or sprouted sunflower seed and a little canary seed and/or oats.

4   Mixture of small seeds: canary, oats, safflower and a little hemp; spray millet; limited sunflower seed, dry, soaked or sprouted; sprouting pulses such as mung beans, cooked butterbeans and lentils; boiled maize; green leaves of spinach, Swiss chard, lettuce, sowthistle, dandelion, chickweed, etc.; fresh vegetables daily, including corn, carrot, celery, courgettes (squash or zucchini and similar vegetables), green beans and peas in the pod; fresh fruit daily (see 2 for types); nuts – walnuts, hazelnuts (lightly cracked), pecans and boiled peanuts; cooked chicken on the bone and chop bones.

4a   Without small seeds and nuts, but with whole vegetables such as beet, whole lettuce and cooked potatoes; also cooked meat; cooked rice.

4b   Becomes overweight easily – feed only canary seed and a mixture of millets, soaked and dry, and seeding grasses; oats and boiled maize when rearing young.

5   Mixture of small seeds: canary, millet and smaller amounts of oats, buckwheat, safflower and a little hemp; limited sunflower seed; spray millet; green leaves etc. (see 4) and seeding grasses; rearing food (see 2); apple (other fruits if acceptable).

6   Dried figs after soaking in water for a few hours, two or more per bird daily (preferably one each twice daily) with, once daily, a drop of Konakion (Roche) or other Vitamin K additive; various other fruits (fruit forming at least 50 per cent of diet); soaked sultanas; berries (elder, mountain ash, pyracantha), spray millet; mix-

ture of small seeds (see 4); cooked pulses; rearing food (see 2). Breeding diet: some pairs consume large quantities of mealworms, especially during first 3 weeks of chicks' lives, and also small maggots *well cleaned*; proprietary insectivorous food. Australian residents: fresh figs for live insect content; fresh corn, soaked dog food. It is advisable to withhold seed for first 3 weeks of chicks' lives.

7   Fruit – offer any type but especially apple, pear, orange, cactus fruits, grapes, pomegranate, etc., forming about 30 per cent of diet; fresh vegetables, especially carrot, celery, green peas and beans; fresh corn, etc.; also green leaves (see 2); spray millet; mixture of small seeds (see 5); soaked and sprouted sunflower seed; cooked beans and pulses and boiled maize; cubes of hard cheese, dry or semi-sweet biscuits; cooked chicken or chop bones.

7a   Without chicken and chop bones.

7b   As 7a but some birds show little enthusiasm for fresh vegetables.

8   Cooked beans and pulses, boiled maize; sunflower seed – dry, soaked or sprouted – but limited for Greys; fruit, especially apple, orange, grapes, banana; rearing food (see 2); various fresh vegetables – but some will consume only fresh corn; dry or semi-sweet biscuits; spray millet; cooked chicken or chop bones relished by some birds.

9   Mixture of small seeds, mainly canary, millet and oats; a little hemp in cold weather; apple; green leaves, etc. (see 4); willow catkins; spray millet; rearing food (see 2) when rearing young.

10   Fruits such as apple and pear, cut into halves, not chopped; also grapes, and fruits in season such as pomegranate, guavas and cactus fruits, and berries such as blackberries and redcurrants; small seeds such as canary, but especially soaked oats; spray millet; sponge cake and nectar; insectivorous mixture; mealworms, maggots and ant pupae.

11   Soaked or sprouted sunflower seed; walnuts, peanuts, pecans, Brazil nuts, pine nuts; fresh corn, boiled maize; banana, orange, grapes; slices of wholemeal bread; cubes of cheese. Tame birds can be offered nutritious items from the table, but fatty or salted foods should be avoided. In tropical and subtropical regions, palm fruits can be given.

12   Soaked or sprouted sunflower seed; walnuts, pine nuts, pecans; fresh corn, boiled maize; fruit and vegetables. In tropical or subtropical regions, palm fruits should be given.

13   Mixture of soaked or sprouted sunflower seed; boiled maize; cooked butter beans or sprouted mung beans; cooked whole rice; chopped fresh vegetables such as carrot, green beans and/or courgettes (zucchini); fresh fruits such as apple, orange, grapes and banana in a separate container; a mixture of small seeds (canary, oats and a little hemp) in another container. Nutritious items from the table, except fatty or salted foods, can also be offered.

14   Mixture of small seeds; sunflower seed (limited); walnuts, peanuts, pine nuts; fresh corn; apple and other fruits; cooked chicken bones with some meat; berries of hawthorn (*Crataegus monogyna*), cotoneaster and pyracantha.

15   Fruits such as banana, papaya, apple, pear, cactus fruits and carrots – best given spiked on to nails on a perch; also bread and milk; fruit in nectar and rearing food made with hard-boiled egg, carrot, non-fat cheese and wholegrain bread; raw egg added to bread and milk when rearing young.

All seed-eating species should have, in addition, access to mineral blocks, and all parrots except large macaws and cockatoos (which usually destroy it immediately) well-cleaned cuttlefish bone.

Incubation
The most usual incubation period is given. This can vary as a result of the incubation habits of the individual bird and is also influenced by environmental factors such as climate. Unless otherwise stated, only the female of the species incubates.

Young in Nest
Widely varying periods can be recorded in the same species, influenced by diet, climate and even the type of nest used.

Sexual Dimorphism
Where this is slight, it can be more marked in some individuals than in others.

CITES
Convention on International Trade in Endangered Species of Wild Flora and Fauna (sometimes known as the Washington Convention) regulates trade, classifying fauna into three appendices. Those on Appendix 1 are the most endangered and trade in species on this appendix (wild-caught and captive-bred) is strictly controlled.

ILLUSTRATIONS
Each species is illustrated and, unless otherwise stated in the text, it is a male of the nominate race which appears in the photograph.

FOR GREATER ACCURACY IN FUTURE EDITIONS
Basic reproduction data on some species of parrots is not well documented. This applies not only to species which are rare in aviculture but also to some fairly common ones. For some species in the pages which follow, the incubation period or the period the young spend in the nest is followed by an asterisk (*). This means that more data is needed to determine the period or range of periods (they can vary under different conditions). If you are an aviculturist with precise data for the species marked, please correspond with the author, c/o Blandford Press, Villiers House, 41/47 Strand, London WC2N 5JE. Your valuable assistance will be acknowledged in future editions, which will be substantially improved with the cooperation of aviculturists.

Please note that the incubation period is calculated from the laying of the last egg in the clutch to the hatching of that egg, and that unless eggs are numbered as laid, or all the eggs in the clutch hatch, or the eggs are artificially incubated from day 1, it is impossible to obtain the exact incubation period.

PARROT SPECIES

Rajah Lory   *Chalcopsitta atra insignis*

German Sammetlori   **Dutch** Rajahlori

Length 30 cm (12 in).
Weight 220 g (7½ oz).
Immatures Less red – mainly on lores
(thus easily confused with *C. atra
atra*); white bare skin surrounding eye
and lower mandible; iris brownish.
Origin Western New Guinea (eastern
Vogelkop, Onin and Bomberai
peninsulas). Black Lory (*C. atra atra*):
extreme western New Guinea (western
Vogelkop and Irian Jaya); islands of
Batanta and Salawati.

Status Fairly common in open
habitats.
Aviculture *C. a. insignis* rarely
available and only since late 1980s;
nominate race since 1970; breeding
limited but increasing.
Accommodation 1.
Diet 2.
Clutch size 2.
Incubation 25 days.
Young in nest 10 to 11 weeks; sexually
mature at about 3 years.

This is one of the most intelligent and affectionate of all lories.

Duivenbode's Lory *Chalcopsitta duivenbodei*

German Braunlori   **Dutch** Duivenbodelori

Length 31 cm (12½ in).
Weight 230 g (8 oz).
Immatures Yellow, duller and less extensive on face and bend of wing; elongated nape feathers brown (not yellow); white bare skin surrounding eye and lower mandible; iris brownish.
Origin Northern New Guinea from Geelvink Bay, Irian Jaya, east to Astrolabe Bay.

Status Common to uncommon (lowlands only).
Aviculture Occasionally available since early 1970s; limited but increasing breeding.
Accommodation 1.
Diet 2.
Clutch size 2.
Incubation 24 days.
Young in nest 11 weeks.

This lory's most striking feature – yellow under-wing coverts – is seen only when it flies. Like the Black Lory, it has a very loud voice, but great charm and beauty.

Yellow-streaked Lory   *Chalcopsitta scintillata*

German Schimmerlori   **Dutch** Geelgestreepte lori

Length 30 cm (12 in).
Weight 195–210 g (7–7½ oz); newly hatched chicks weigh 8 g (¼ oz).
Immatures Forehead and crown black; plumage variable – duller or even brighter (young from author's pair with bright-orange streaking on breast and neck); white bare skin surrounding eye and lower mandible; iris brown; brown-yellow markings at base of upper mandible.

Origin Southern New Guinea; Aru Islands (southern Moluccas, Indonesia).
Status Common in lowland areas.
Aviculture Available since early 1970s; fairly frequent breeding.
Accommodation 1.
Diet 2.
Clutch size 2.
Incubation 24 days.
Young in nest 11–13 weeks.

As with preceding 2 species, they usually nest twice or more annually. Nominate race has under-wing coverts, mainly red, with yellow and in some birds green; *C. s. chloroptera* has under-wing coverts mainly green, with little or no yellow and red.

Cardinal Lory *Chalcopsitta cardinalis*

German Kardinallori   **Dutch** Kardinaalori

Length 30 cm (12 in).
Weight 200 g (7 oz).
Immatures Paler above, usually with lighter margins to the feathers or underparts; beak and iris brown.
Origin Solomon Islands (south-west Pacific); various small islands such as Tanga, Lihir and Tabor group.
Status Common, often in very large flocks.

Aviculture Always very rare (Solomons have never permitted commercial export of fauna); breeding has occurred.
Accommodation 1.
Diet 2.
Clutch size 2.
Incubation 24 days.
Young in nest Unknown but assume about 11 weeks.

In 1990 permission was granted for a few Cardinal Lories to be exported. If this occurs, the species could be established in aviculture.

Black-winged Lory *Eos cyanogenia*

German Blauohrlori **Dutch** Koningslori

Length 28 cm (11 in).
Weight 160 g (5½ oz).
Immatures Red feathers margined with purple-black; beak and iris brown.
Origin Indonesia – Biak, Supiori and other islands of Geelvink Bay, Irian Jaya.
Status Locally common in coastal areas where deforestation has not occurred; threatened by destruction of habitat.

Aviculture Occasionally available during 1970s and 1980s; limited breeding – except by a single UK partnership which has reared enough to ensure the species is established there, using unrelated pairs.
Accommodation 1.
Diet 2.
Clutch size 2.
Incubation 25 days.
Young in nest 75–87 days.

Because of its potentially endangered status, this is a good choice for the concerned and responsible aviculturist whose aim goes beyond breeding solely for enjoyment.

Violet-necked Lory *Eos squamata squamata*

German Kapuzenlori   **Dutch** Violetneklori

Length 25 cm (10 in).
Weight 110 g (4 oz).
Immatures Colours less clear-cut; feathers of underparts margined with purple; white skin surrounding eye; beak and iris brown.
Origin Indonesia, western Papuan islands (Gebe, Waigeu, Batanta, Misool) and Schildpad Islands. *E. s. riciniata* (violet-grey collar, extending to hind-crown in some birds) is from northern Moluccas and Weda islands.
Status Fairly common in a variety of habitats.
Aviculture Long available, common and free-breeding.
Accommodation 1.
Diet 3.
Clutch size 2.
Incubation 25 days.
Young in nest 9 weeks.

Obi Violet-necked Lory   *Eos squamata obiensis*

Information as for Violet-necked Lory   **Weight** 90 g (3 oz).
(page 23). except: **Origin** Indonesia, northern Moluccan
Length 22 cm (9 in).   islands, Obi only.

Either unknown or unnoticed in aviculture until 1987, it is distinguished by black scapulars, the absence of neck markings (or a few scattered mauve feathers) and its small size. It is sometimes incorrectly called 'Wallace's Lory'.

Blue-streaked Lory *Eos reticulata*

German Strichellori   **Dutch** Blauwgestreepte lori

Length 31 cm (12 in).
Weight 160 g (5½ oz).
Immatures Feathers of underparts broadly edged with blue-black, giving overall darker appearance; wing markings less clearly defined; white eye skin; beak and iris brown.
Origin Indonesia – Tanimbar Islands, southern Moluccas.
Status Formerly common (still common on Yamdena island in 1981), its population has suffered due to mass trapping and deforestation.
Aviculture Rare until 1971, when large-scale trapping commenced (between 1984 and 1985 1,000 were exported to Taiwan alone); gradually declining availability and limited breeding.
Accommodation 1.
Diet 2.
Clutch size 2.
Incubation 25 days.
Young in nest 12 weeks.

Roland Wirth (1990) emphasized the necessity of *coordinated* breeding programmes for certain Indonesian parrots, including Blue-streaked and Black-winged Lories (*E. cyanogenia*, page 22): 'Successful breeding of parrots in aviaries is only the first step towards their conservation. If this is not followed by a coordinated management programme, all efforts to save a certain species by means of captive breeding will have been in vain.'

Red or Moluccan Lory *Eos bornea*

German Rotlori   **Dutch** Rode lori

Length About 28 cm (11 in).
Weight 170 g (6 oz).
Immatures Variable – some or most feathers of underparts tinged or edged with blue; some birds have blue ear coverts; white skin surrounding eye; bill brown in nestlings, changing to brownish-orange even before they leave nest; iris greyish.
Origin Indonesia – islands of Ceram, Amboina (Ambon), Saparua, Buru, Goram, Ceramlaut, and Watubela and Kai islands.
Status Common in coastal areas with flowering trees.
Aviculture Always common; free-breeding.
Accommodation 1.
Diet 3.
Clutch size 2.
Incubation 24 days.
Young in nest 9 or 10 weeks. Plucking of chicks by parents almost invariably occurs.

Nominate race (*E. b. bornea*) is illustrated; 3 other sub-species are recognized: *E. b. rothschildi* is slightly smaller (from Ceram), *E. b. bernsteini* slightly larger (Kai islands) and *E. b. cyanonothus* from Buru (darker red).

Dusky Lory *Pseudeos fuscata*

German Weissbürzellori   **Dutch** Witruglori

Length 25 cm (10 in).
Weight 155 g (5½ oz); newly hatched chicks 7 g (¼ oz).
Immatures Colours duller, less well defined; areas of brown and orange variable, also rump colour; greyish skin surrounding lower mandible; bill and iris brownish, both soon changing to orange.
Origin New Guinea, distributed almost throughout; Salawati (western Papuan islands) and Japen Island in Geelvink Bay.
Status Locally common, up to 2,000 m (6,600 ft); often occurs in large flocks.
Aviculture Rare until 1972, when commercial export commenced; readily available; free-breeding.
Accommodation 1.
Diet 3.
Clutch size 2.
Incubation 24 days.
Young in nest 10 weeks.

Unusually for lories, it is a seasonal nester, laying in April or May and producing a second clutch only if the first fails (or young removed). There are 2 colour phases, orange (most common in aviculture) and yellow (illustrated).

Ornate Lorikeet   *Trichoglossus ornatus*

German Schmucklori   **Dutch** Ornaatlori

Length 25 cm (10 in).
Weight 95 g (3½ oz).
Immatures A young bird is
illustrated, with more yellow on
abdomen and less pronounced barring
on upper breast than an adult; cere
and skin surrounding eye are
blue-tinged pale grey (in adults, dark
blue-grey); iris brown in very young
birds, red in adults.
Origin Indonesia – Sulawesi (Celebes)
and larger offshore islands.

Status Common in wooded areas,
except dense forest.
Aviculture Imported mainly during
early 1970s; now uncommon; breeding
limited but increasing (nearly died out
in aviculture).
Accommodation 1.
Diet 2.
Clutch size 2.
Incubation 25 days.
Young in nest About 9 weeks.

Green-naped Lorikeet *Trichoglossus haematodus haematodus*

German Breitbindenlori   **Dutch** Groenneklori

Length 27 cm (10½ in).
Weight 130 g (4½ oz); newly hatched chicks 5 g (⅙ oz).
Immatures Head coloration much duller – dark brown-blue, with blue as in adults only on forehead, and green shaft-streaking on forepart of crown; pale-grey skin surrounding eye; beak and iris brown.
Origin New Guinea, western coastal region; Indonesian islands of Amboina, Buru, Ceram, Ceramlaut; Goram, Watubela and western Papuan islands; islands in Geelvink Bay (not Biak).
Status One of most widespread and conspicuous lories of Eastern Highlands, and other regions of New Guinea, occurring up to 1,500 m (5,000 ft) in primary forest and 2,000 m (6,600 ft) in the casuarina groves and trees of villages and open country.
Aviculture Most common and inexpensive member of genus; free-breeding.
Accommodation 1.
Diet 3.
Clutch size 2.
Incubation 24 days.
Young in nest 8 weeks.

Many pairs will produce 4 clutches a year if chicks are removed (sometimes necessary if chicks are plucked). Its prolificacy and hardiness make this an ideal species for the beginner.

Mitchell's Lorikeet *Trichoglossus haematodus mitchellii*

German Mitchell's-Lori   **Dutch** Mitchell-lori

Information as for Green-naped Lorikeet (page 29) except:
Length 23 cm (9 in).
Weight 100 g (3½ oz).
Immatures Duller plumage; white cere and skin surrounding eye; beak and iris brown.
Origin Indonesia – islands of Bali and Lombok in the Lesser Sundas.

Status Formerly common; no information on present status.
Aviculture Irregularly exported, now seldom available; limited breeding and in danger of dying out in aviculture.
Sexual dimorphism Male's breast is solid scarlet; female's has a yellow tinge.

Forsten's Lorikeet *Trichoglossus haematodus forsteni*

German Forsten's-Lori   **Dutch** Forstenlori

Information as for Green-naped Lorikeet (page 29) except:
Length 23 cm (9 in).
Weight 100 g (3½ oz).
Immatures Almost as colourful as parents; distinguished from young of nominate race by almost total absence of dark margins to breast feathers;

white cere and skin surrounding eye; beak and iris brown.
Origin Indonesia – Sumbawa Island.
Status No recent information.
Aviculture Fairly frequently available; free-breeding – a pair in author's care produced 15 chicks in 18 months.

Weber's Lorikeet *Trichoglossus haematodus weberi*

German Weber's-Lori   **Dutch** Weberlori

Information as for Green-naped Lorikeet (page 29) except:
Length 23 cm (9 in).
Weight 85 g (3 oz).
Immatures Beak is reddish-brown or reddish-black (Kyme, 1971, suggested this might be a sexual distinction);

iris brown.
Origin Indonesia – Flores Island, up to 1,200 m (4,000 ft)
Status No recent information.
Aviculture Always rare; in the USA it has been established by a single specialist breeder.

Edwards' Lorikeet   *Trichoglossus haematodus capistratus*

German Blauwangenlori   **Dutch** Bloedvleklori

Information as for Green-naped Lorikeet (page 29) except for:
Length 27 cm (10½ in).
Weight 130 g (4½ oz).
Immatures Beak and iris brown.
Origin Indonesia – Timor Island.
Status No recent information due to political situation.
Aviculture Common during 1970s, now limited availability; limited breeding; note that under-wing coverts are orange and yellow; in *T. h. flavotectus* yellow only and breast is less yellow.

Rosenberg's Lorikeet   *Trichoglossus haematodus rosenbergii*

German Rosenberg's-Allfarblori   **Dutch** Rosenberglori

Information as for Green-naped Lorikeet (page 29) except:
Length 30 cm (12 in).
Weight 150 g (5½ oz) estimated.
Origin Indonesia – the island of Biak in Geelvink Bay, Irian Jaya.
Status Unknown, but as an inhabitant of deep forest confined to a single island, it is extremely vulnerable to deforestation.
Aviculture Almost unknown until 1988, when a few reached Europe and USA.

Massena's Lorikeet   *Trichoglossus haematodus massena*

German Schmalbindenlori   **Dutch** Massenalori

Information as for Green-naped Lorikeet (page 29) except:
Length 25 cm (10 in).
Weight 110 g (4 oz).
Immatures White cere and skin surrounding eye; beak and iris brown.

Origin Solomon Islands, New Hebrides and Bismarck Archipelago, New Guinea.
Status Common in lowland areas.
Aviculture Occasionally imported during 1960s and 1970s; now rare.

The rich-brown nape is its most distinctive feature.

Swainson's or Blue Mountain Lorikeet
Trichoglossus haematodus moluccanus

German Gebirgslori   **Dutch** Lori van de Blauwe Bergen

Information as for Green-naped Lorikeet (page 29) except:
Length 30 cm (12 in).
Weight 130 g ($4\frac{1}{2}$ oz).
Immatures Plumage duller with more yellow on breast; white cere and skin surrounding eye; beak and iris brown.
Origin Eastern Australia from Cape York Peninsula south to Tasmania and Kangaroo Island and to Eyre Peninsula, South Australia; introduced to Perth area, Western Australia.

Status Common in northern part of range, less so in south; found in all types of habitat with trees, including parks and gardens.
Aviculture Well known until Australia banned the export of fauna in 1959; no longer common outside Australia; some strains are inbred.
Clutch size 2.
Incubation 23 days.
Young in nest 8–9 weeks; sexually mature before 2 years.

Red-collared Lorikeet *Trichoglossus haematodus rubritorquis*

German Rotnackenlori   **Dutch** Roodneklori

Information as for Green-naped Lorikeet (page 29) except:
Length 30 cm (12 in).
Weight 130 g (4½ oz).
Immatures Duller, with narrower orange collar.
Origin Northern Australia from Kimberley division of Western Australia, east to Gulf of Carpentaria, Queensland.
Status Common, but nomadic in response to food supply.
Aviculture Common and popular in first half of 20th century; now rare outside Australia; limited breeding.

Meyer's Lorikeet   *Trichoglossus flavoviridis meyeri*

German Meyer's-Lori   **Dutch** Meyerlori

Length 17 cm (6 in).
Weight 50 g (2 oz); newly hatched chicks 3 or 4 g (about $\frac{1}{10}$ oz).
Immatures Dark edges to feathers of underparts less well defined; yellow bases to mantle feathers more conspicuous; head coloration variable; beak and iris brown.
Origin Indonesia – Sulawesi (Celebes).
Status Common and widespread in forest, but this could deteriorate.

Aviculture Almost unknown until early 1970s; now fairly readily available and frequently bred.
Accommodation 2.
Diet 3.
Clutch size 2.
Incubation 23 days.
Young in nest 52–54 days.
Sexual dimorphism Forehead and crown golden-olive in male, browner in female; males usually have brighter-yellow ear coverts.

An ideal species for those with little space or close neighbours; its voice is a pleasant warble.

Scaly-breasted Lorikeet *Trichoglossus chlorolepidotus*

German Schuppenlori   **Dutch** Schubbenlori

Length 24 cm (9½ in).
Weight 85 g (3 oz).
Immatures Duller than adults with less yellow on neck and mantle; beak and iris brown.
Origin Eastern Australia from north Queensland south to New South Wales, approximately 100 km (60 miles) south of Sydney; a population in Melbourne area perhaps derived from escaped cage birds.
Status Common, especially in north-east.

Aviculture Well known until Australia banned export of its fauna; now rare outside Australia; limited breeding in Europe and USA.
Accommodation 1.
Diet 2.
Clutch size 2, sometimes 3.
Incubation 22 days.
Young in nest 8 weeks; sexually mature at about 18 months.
Sexual dimorphism Slight, but most males have larger heads with stronger blue tinge.

A pair is illustrated, with male on the left.

Perfect Lorikeet *Trichoglossus euteles*

German Gelbkopflori   **Dutch** Geelkoplori

Length 25 cm (10 in).
Weight 75 g (2½ oz).
Immatures Iris brown; beak dark brown or orange-brown; in young from some pairs this may indicate sex, males having the beak orange-brown.
Origin Indonesia – Timor and Lesser Sunda islands (Lomblen east to Nila and Babar).
Status Not uncommon, especially at higher altitudes (up to 2,300 m, 7,600 ft).
Aviculture Fairly common and free-breeding.
Accommodation 2.
Diet 3.
Clutch size 3.
Incubation 23 days.
Young in nest 8 weeks; sexually mature at or before 1 year.

An ideal species for the beginner or those with limited accommodation. Its voice is less loud and harsh than that of most lories.

Varied Lorikeet *Trichoglossus (or Psitteuteles) versicolor*

German Buntlori   **Dutch** Bonte lori

Length 19 cm (7½ in).
Weight 60 g (2 oz).
Immatures Duller, with crown green or green marked with red. In the wild young have face suffused with red and 'can be readily sexed by the brightness of the red face and ear coverts' (Sindel, 1986). However, aviary-bred young do not have the red face; beak is brownish and iris brownish-grey.
Origin Australia, from Kimberley division of Western Australia to coast of northern Queensland.
Status Common in wooded country, especially near water.
Aviculture Non-existent outside Australia; more widely kept in Australia since 1980s; not readily available; least free-breeding of Australian lorikeets.
Accommodation 1.
Diet 2 (note that it is prone to obesity).
Clutch size 3–5.
Incubation 22 days.
Young in nest 6½–7 weeks.
Sexual dimorphism Mauve-pink on breast less extensive in female, also red on crown; yellow markings are duller.

Unlike other lories from tropical regions, this species seems to be sensitive to cold.

Iris Lorikeet *Trichoglossus iris*

German Irislori   **Dutch** Irislori

Length 18 cm (7 in).
Weight 60 g (2 oz); newly hatched chicks weigh 4 g (about $\frac{1}{10}$ oz).
Immatures Ear coverts bluish-green, crown mainly green; red less extensive; barred breast markings less defined; beak dark brown but changed to orange in some by time of fledging; iris brownish.
Origin Indonesia – Timor and Wetar islands.
Status Probably not common; no recent information due to political situation.
Aviculture Fairly rare; limited breeding.
Accommodation 1.

Diet 3, but consumes more seed, carrot, figs, etc.
Clutch size 2.
Incubation 23 days.
Young in nest Average 8 weeks, but 48 to 67 days recorded by author – the earlier they leave nest, the less time they spend out for the first few days. Breeders should aim for parent-reared birds, as those hand-reared imprint very easily and must be placed with their own species as soon as independent. Potential life-span 25 years or more; author has had two wild-caught birds for 20 years and the female ceased to lay at 18 years.

Goldie's Lorikeet *Trichoglossus goldiei*

German Veilchenlori   **Dutch** Viooltjeslori

Length 19 cm (7 in).
Weight 45 g (1½ oz).
Immatures Forehead and forepart of crown dull-plum colour, rear part of crown dull bluish indistinctly streaked with black; colours duller throughout; cere lighter, beak brownish; iris greyish-brown.
Origin New Guinea, central mountainous part from Weyland Mountains, Irian Jaya, to south-eastern Papua New Guinea.
Status Generally uncommon but locally numerous at mid-mountain elevations in flocks.
Aviculture Almost unknown until 1977; now readily available and free-breeding.
Accommodation 2.
Diet 3.
Clutch size 2.
Incubation 23 days.
Young in nest 8 weeks; sexually mature at 1 year.
Sexual dimorphism Slight, but males are usually brighter violet on head, with more extensive red.

This has become the most popular of small lories, cherished for its beauty, inoffensive voice and readiness to breed.

Black-capped Lory   *Lorius lory*

German Frauenlori   **Dutch** Zwartkaplori

Length 31 cm (12½ in).
Weight 195 g (7 oz); newly hatched chicks 8 g (¼ oz).
Immatures Duller, with less well-defined colours, lacking the strong sheen of adults; upper breast red and abdomen blackish-blue; beak and iris brownish.
Origin New Guinea, western Papuan islands (nominate race occurs on Waigeu, Batanta, Salawati and Misool), islands in Geelvink Bay.
Status Locally common to uncommon, in forest (never in second growth – unlike many lories), usually in pairs or trios, never in flocks.
Aviculture Common until the 1960s, gradually becoming rarer as export ceased; in mid-1980s only 50 birds survived in UK; bred in limited but increasing numbers.
Accommodation 1.
Diet 2.
Clutch size 2.
Incubation 25 days.
Young in nest 9–10 weeks.

The nominate race is illustrated (best known in aviculture); also known is *L. l. erythrothorax*, with upper breast entirely red and less blue on abdomen and hind neck. This species has perhaps the most attractive voice of all large lories and is also a talented mimic.

Purple-bellied Lory *Lorius hypoinochrous*

German Schwarzsteisslori   **Dutch** Violetstaartlori

Length 28 cm (11 in).
Weight 220 g (7½ oz).
Immatures Beak and iris brownish.
Origin South-east New Guinea, also eastern Papuan islands (Misima, Tagula and Rossel in Louisiade Archipelago); Trobriand and Woodlark islands in Bismarck and D'Entrecasteaux archipelagos.
Status Apparently common throughout its range, in a variety of habitats – primary and secondary forest, partially cleared areas and plantations.
Aviculture Extremely rare; no recent records outside natural habitat.
Accommodation 1.
Diet 2.
Clutch size Not known but probably 2.
Incubation Not known but assume 25 or 26 days.
Young in nest Not known but assume 11 weeks.

The sub-species *L. h. devittatus* is illustrated. It differs from the nominate race in lacking black margins to under-wing coverts. Note the startling white cere.

Yellow-bibbed Lory　*Lorius chlorocercus*

German Grünschwanzlori　　　　**Dutch** Groenstaartlori

Length 24 cm (9½ in).
Weight 150 g (5½ oz).
Immatures Little or no yellow on upper breast; whitish skin surrounding eye; beak and iris brown.
Origin Solomon Islands (except Bougainville).
Status Fairly common in a variety of habitats – in pairs or groups.

Aviculture Always rare; limited breeding, mainly New Zealand, also Germany and Tenerife.
Accommodation 1.
Diet 3.
Clutch size 2.
Incubation 25 days.
Young in nest Unknown, probably 10 or 11 weeks.

Personality of this species is extrovert, cheerful and cheeky. They have a quite melodious whistle and, to the unwary, a far from pleasant nip! Males, whether wild-caught or captive-bred, seem to delight in biting.

Purple-capped Lory *Lorius domicellus*

German Erzlori   **Dutch** Purperkaplori, Vrouwenlori

Length 28 cm (11 in).
Weight 235 g ($8\frac{1}{2}$ oz).
Immatures Purple on nape more extensive; cere black, skin around eye greyish; beak and iris brown.
Origin Indonesia – Ceram; almost certainly extinct on Amboina by the 1980s due to extensive deforestation; introduced to Buru but not known to occur there now.
Status Rare and declining.
Aviculture Formerly uncommon, now rare; captive population in 1990 was believed to be as follows: Netherlands, about 12 pairs; Switzerland, 10 pairs; Germany, about 10 birds; Loro Parque, Tenerife, 2 pairs; Singapore, 8 pairs plus 4 young; USA, maximum 12 birds – total, 90 birds; limited breeding.
Accommodation 1.
Diet 2.
Clutch size 2.
Incubation 26 days.
Young in nest Few reports of parent-reared young, but widely differing in periods of 65–95 days; probably 11 weeks is normal.

In Germany, Zoologischen Gesellschaft für Arten- und Populationsschutz is attempting to coordinate a breeding programme among zoos and private breeders. Worldwide cooperation is needed.

Chattering Lory *Lorius garrulus*

German Gelbmantellori   **Dutch** Molukkenlori

Length 30 cm (12 in).
Weight 200 g (7 oz).
Immatures Beak brown, iris dark brownish.
Origin Indonesia – northern Moluccas islands. Nominate race: Halmahera and the Weda islands; *L. g. flavopalliatus*: Batjan and Obi; *L. g. morotaianus* (yellow on mantle duller and intermediate in extent between other two sub-species): Morotai.

Status Locally common except near settlements; decline due to trapping noted, particularly on Halmahera.
Aviculture Formerly common, now less so; fairly frequent breeding.
Accommodation 1.
Diet 2.
Clutch size 2.
Incubation 26 days.
Young in nest 10–11 weeks.

Nominate race is illustrated. Equally well known is *L. g. flavopalliatus*, the Yellow-backed Lory. Extremely aggressive, this species must never be kept with other birds. It is intelligent, beautiful and playful and some are good mimics.

Tahiti Blue Lory *Vini peruviana*

German Saphirlori   **Dutch** Safierlori

Length 14 cm (5½ in).
Weight 33 g (1 oz); newly hatched chicks weigh 2 g ($\frac{1}{15}$ oz).
Immatures Dull bluish above, brighter on head; no white 'bib' but a few greyish-white feathers at side of beak – first white feathers appear at about 5 months; underparts dull blue-grey; feet and beak black and iris greyish.
Origin Society Islands, Pacific: Scilly and Bellingshausen (extinct on Tahiti and most other Society Islands); atolls in the Tuamotu – mainly Rangiroa, also Aitutaki, Cook Islands (probably introduced).

Status Rare; about 1,000 birds believed to survive; they nest in coconut palms – easily accessible to rats, which prey on eggs and young.
Aviculture An extreme rarity (no commercial export); at time of writing known in 4 collections worldwide.
Accommodation Small planted house (heated to about 15°C, 59°F).
Diet 1, plus sweet-corn, pomegranates in season.
Clutch size 2.
Incubation 25 days by male and female.
Young in nest 9 weeks.

Ultramarine Lory *Vini ultramarina*

German Smaragdlori   **Dutch** Smaragdlori

Length 16 cm (6 in).
Weight Estimated 35 g ($1\frac{1}{4}$ oz).
Immatures White areas replaced by bluish-black, marked with greyish-white; plumage is mainly dark blue with pale blue on sides of abdomen; feet and beak black and iris dark brown.
Origin Marquesas Islands in central Pacific – islands of Nukuhiva and Huapu; introduced to Uahuka (Marquesas).
Status Rare especially on Nukuhiva; rapid decline throughout range between 1985 and 1990: 'slipping to the edge of extinction' (R. Wirth, in litt., 1991).
Aviculture An extreme rarity, never exported commercially; at time of writing, possibly only a single bird outside native islands.
Accommodation See Tahiti Blue Lory, page 49.
Diet 1.
Clutch size 2.
Incubation Probably 25 days, by male and female.
Young in nest About 8 weeks.

This is one of the world's most beautiful and unusually marked gems which has long excited the interest of aviculturists, to whom it is never likely to be available.

Musk Lorikeet *Glossopsitta concinna*

German Moschuslori   **Dutch** Muskuslori

Length 22 cm (9 in).
Weight 60 g (2 oz).
Immatures Duller, brick-red or orange-red on forehead and ear coverts and red less extensive; adult head colour acquired at about 6 months; beak brown, tipped orange by age of 3 months; iris brownish.
Origin Australia, east and south-east from north Queensland (Bowen district) to South Australia (Spencer Gulf region); Tasmania, eastern half.
Status Apparently common, but nomadic; decline possibly occurring due to loss of nest sites when land is cleared for agriculture.
Aviculture Rare outside Australia but since the mid-1980s being bred in Rotterdam Zoo, Netherlands and, since 1990, at Chester Zoo, UK; also a small number in USA; fairly common in Australian aviaries.
Accommodation 1.
Diet 3.
Clutch size 2.
Incubation 22 days average but marked variation.
Young in nest 7 weeks; sexually mature by 18 months.

Little Lorikeet *Glossopsitta pusilla*

German Zwergmoschuslori   **Dutch** Dwerglori

Length 15 cm (6 in).
Weight 45 g (1½ oz).
Immatures Duller plumage; beak and iris dark brown.
Origin Eastern and south-eastern Australia from north Queensland (Cairns district) to South Australia (York Peninsula), sometimes reaching north-eastern Tasmania.
Status Locally common and nomadic; decline possibly occurring due to loss of nest sites when land is cleared for agriculture.
Aviculture Unknown outside Australia since 1959 export ban; rarely bred in Australian aviaries before 1980s.
Accommodation 1.
Diet 1.
Clutch size 3–5 .
Incubation 20 days.
Young in nest 6 weeks.

Unlike other lorikeets, it is so gentle and inoffensive it can even be kept with finches.

Purple-crowned Lorikeet *Glossopsitta porphyrocephala*

German Porphyrkopflori   **Dutch** Purperkroonlori

Length 15 cm (6 in).
Weight 45 g (1½ oz).
Immatures Duller, especially on face – red absent and purple crown reduced or absent; cere and eye skin paler; adult plumage acquired at 5 months.
Origin Extreme southern Australia except the Nullarbor Plain, as far north as Shark Bay, Western Australia, to Eden, New South Wales and on occasions as far north as southern Queensland (Sindel, 1986).
Status Plentiful except in extreme parts of range; sometimes in large flocks.
Aviculture Always rare outside Australia, it has been totally unknown for more than 20 years; in Australian aviculture is now more widely obtainable and breeding freely.
Accommodation 1.
Diet 1.
Clutch size 3 or 4.
Incubation 20 days.
Young in nest 7½ weeks; sexually mature at only 6 months (Sindel, 1986).

It can be bred on colony system. Sindel described it as the most prolific and successful in aviaries of the small Australian lorikeets.

Striated Lorikeet   *Charmosyna multistriata*

German Vielstrichellori   **Dutch** Veelstrepenlori

Length 18 cm (7 in).
Weight 40 g (1½ oz).
Immatures Darker green on head, smaller orange spots on nape and duller streaks on underparts; beak bluish grey and iris brownish.
Origin Western New Guinea, on southern slopes of main ranges between Snow Mountains and upper Fly River.
Status Unknown; it has been found at few localities, mainly at altitudes between 180 m (600 ft) and 1,800 m (6,000 ft)
Aviculture Unknown until late 1970s, very rarely available; young reared in only 1 or 2 collections.
Accommodation 1.
Diet 1, plus soft fruits (pear, peach).
Clutch size 2.
Incubation 25 days.
Young in nest 7½ weeks.
Sexual dimorphism Males have more orange than yellow on back of head.

It is, perhaps, reminiscent of Goldie's Lorikeet (page 43), suggesting that the latter could be a link between the two genera.

Wilhelmina's Lorikeet *Charmosyna wilhelminae*

German Wilhelminenlori   **Dutch** Wilhelminalori

Length 13 cm (5 in).
Weight Estimated 20 g ($\frac{2}{3}$ oz).
Immatures Little or no streaking on crown and breast; males have red under-wing coverts and red band across underside of flight feathers as in adults, but back is dull purple (red in adults).
Origin Central highlands of New Guinea, up to about 2,200 m (7,300 ft).
Status Local, depending on availability of pollen and nectar, in montane forest and forest edges, in flocks as large as 100 or more.

Aviculture Very rare; privately imported into Britain twice during early years of 20th century; since then the importation of only a single bird (the one depicted) is known to the author.
Accommodation 2.
Diet 1.
Clutch size Assume 2.
Incubation Assume 23 days.
Young in nest Assume about 7 weeks.
Sexual dimorphism Male is illustrated; female has lower back and under-wing coverts green.

Red-spotted Lorikeet   *Charmosyna rubronotata*

German Rotbürzellori   **Dutch** Roodstuitlori

Length 15 cm (6 in).
Weight 30 g (1 oz).
Immatures Male and female similar to adult male but no red on body; at three months faint yellow streaks start to appear on female's ear coverts.
Origin North-west New Guinea, as far east as Astrolabe Bay; Indonesia – islands of Biak in Geelvink Bay, and Salawati.
Status Apparently not common but little is known; occurs in small flocks.
Aviculture Unknown until late 1970s, when a few birds reached Europe; since then a very small number has been imported into Europe and USA; first breeding occurred in 1991.
Accommodation 2.
Diet 1.
Clutch size 2.
Incubation Assume 23 days.
Young in nest Assume about 7 weeks.
Sexual dimorphism Female lacks red on head, has ear coverts green streaked with yellowish-green; under-wing coverts and sides of breast pale green.

Red-flanked or Pleasing Lorikeet *Charmosyna placentis*

German Schönlori   **Dutch** Roodflanklori

Length 17 cm (7 in).
Weight 37 g (1¼ oz).
Immatures Variable, perhaps
dependent on sub-species (and in
captivity 2 different sub-species might
be paired together); however, all young
can be sexed at 4 weeks by the
presence (males) or absence (females)
of red feathers on flanks. Most young
have red on cheeks and some males
have yellow streaks on ear coverts. Feet
are brownish-pink; beak and iris are
brownish, changing to pink soon after
leaving nest.
Origin New Guinea, except central
part; islands of Moluccas (Ceram,
Amboina, Ambelau, Pandjang and
Obi); western Papuan islands;
Woodlark Island (east of New
Guinea), throughout the Bismarck

Archipelago to the easternmost
Admiralty Islands and to Bougainville
(Solomon Islands) and Buku and
Nugurua islands.
Status Common and widespread in
forests, woodlands and plantations.
Aviculture Almost unknown until late
1970s; available in small numbers;
free-breeding in warm climates or
indoor birdrooms.
Accommodation 2.
Diet 1 plus soaked figs and sultanas;
some like spray millet.
Clutch size 2.
Incubation 23 days (in incubator);
male and female incubate but seldom
commence until several days after eggs
are laid.
Young in nest About 7 weeks.

Most common sub-species are nominate, *C. p. subplacens* (illustrated – has green
rump, not blue – with female behind male) and *C. p. intensior*.

Fairy Lorikeet　*Charmosyna pulchella*

German Goldstrichellori　　　**Dutch** Zwartstuitlori

Length 18 cm (7 in).
Weight 35 g (1¼ oz).
Immatures Crown dull green, in nominate race, upper breast dull green without yellow streaks, female's sides yellow, flanks lacking yellow streaks; sexable by 30 days; beak dark brown, soon changing to dull coral; feet greyish-pink and iris brown.
Origin New Guinea, central (mountainous) region.
Status Fairly common to scarce, in pairs, groups or flocks.
Aviculture Almost unknown until 1973, since when it has been imported into Europe and USA in small numbers; limited but increasing breeding.
Accommodation 2.
Diet 1.
Clutch size 2.
Incubation 25 days, by male and female.
Young in nest 8½ weeks – very small on fledging (as in *C. placentis*, page 57).
Sexual dimorphism Female has yellow patches at side of rump; in *C. p. rothschildi* underside of tail is bright yellow in male, greenish-yellow in female.

This and the *Vini* species are the least hardy of the lories and should be wintered indoors, except in hot climates. Illustrated is nominate race (right) and *C. p. rothschildi* (left).

Josephine's Lorikeet *Charmosyna josefinae*

German Josephinenlori   **Dutch** Josephinelori

Length 24 cm (9½ in).
Weight 70 g (2½ oz).
Immatures Colours less clearly
defined; black on abdomen and nape
tinged with green, also thighs; 5 young
reared by a pair of *C. j. sepikiana* could
not be sexed in nest by presence or
absence of yellow – at 4½ months one
female had some yellow feathers or
yellow at bases of feathers of lower
back, and several larger yellow feathers
on lower rump; feet flesh-coloured;
beak and iris brownish, soon
becoming orange.
Origin New Guinea, central
mountainous area from Vogelkop,
Irian Jaya, east to Western Highlands.

Status Fairly common.
Aviculture Unknown until late 1970s;
fairly rare; limited breeding.
Accommodation 1.
Diet 2.
Clutch size 2.
Incubation 25 days; male and female
incubate.
Young in nest 8 weeks (in one nest –
first 47 days, second 62 days!).
Sexual dimorphism Female of
nominate race (perhaps unknown in
aviculture) has lower back green, male
has lower back red; *sepikiana* female
has lower back and flanks bright
yellow.

Stella's Lorikeet *Charmosyna papou goliathina*

German Stella's Lori   **Dutch** Stellalori

Length About 40 cm (16 in) – tail lengthens with maturity.
Weight 95 g ($3\frac{1}{2}$ oz); 1 newly hatched chick weighed 4 g (about $\frac{1}{10}$ oz).
Immatures Duller with blackish margins to red feathers of neck and breast; variable yellow band on underside of secondaries; shorter tail; beak and legs brownish–orange; iris brownish.
Origin New Guinea, mountains of south-east (nominate race, *C. p. papou*); *C. p. goliathina* (with yellow-tipped tail) occurs in mountains of central New Guinea (best known in aviculture).
Status Fairly common – in pairs or small groups.
Aviculture Rare until mid-1970s; limited availability; breeding increasingly successful.
Accommodation 1.
Diet 2.
Clutch size 2.
Incubation 26 days or more – by male and female; does not commence for several days
Young in nest 60 days.
Sexual dimorphism Lower back and sides of rump yellow in female.
Melanism Black-plumaged birds are as numerous, or more so, than red; male distinguished by red flanks (and under-tail coverts in some birds).

Musschenbroek's Lorikeet   *Neopsittacus musschenbroekii*

German Gualori   **Dutch** Musschenbroeklori

Length 20 cm (8 in).
Weight 50 g (1½ oz): newly hatched chicks 4 g (about $\frac{1}{10}$ oz).
Immatures Less brown on head and less red on breast; iris brown, also the beak, the latter changing to yellow before 3 months.
Origin New Guinea, central mountainous part, from the Vogelkop, Irian Jaya, to southern Papua New Guinea.
Status Locally common in and near forest; in Eastern Highlands, for example, widespread at 1,600 m (5,300 ft) to 2,800 m (9,300 ft).
Aviculture Almost unknown until late 1970s; limited availability; breeding limited but increasing.
Accommodation 1.
Diet 3, plus dried figs – favourite food is walnuts.
Clutch size 2.
Incubation 23 days.
Young in nest 8 weeks.
Sexual dimorphism Male has more extensive and richer brown on head.

Temperament is more aloof than other lories; hand-reared young will bite their feeder! Mention should be made of almost identically coloured Emerald Lorikeet (*N. pullicauda*), smaller with underside of tail green; rare in aviculture.

Palm Cockatoo   *Probosciger aterrimus*

German Arakakadu, Palmkakadu   **Dutch** Palmkaketoe

Length 55–70 cm (22–28 in).
Weight About 900 g (32 oz) but range 600–1,000 g (21–36 oz), according to sex (males heavier) and sub-species; newly hatched chick 18 g ($\frac{2}{3}$ oz).
Immatures Feathers of underparts and under-wing coverts edged with pale yellow in some specimens; skin surrounding eye white; beak whitish and grey.
Origin New Guinea, except central mountainous area; Aru Islands, Indonesia and Cape York Peninsula, northern Australia.
Status Common in remote areas of New Guinea, rare due to hunting near settlements, including on Aru Islands (where legally protected); locally common on Cape York.
Aviculture Uncommon but regularly available in small numbers during the decade from the mid-1970s; stricter legislation from the end of the 1980s ended trade in countries which are members of CITES; limited but increasing breeding.
Accommodation 6.
Diet Nuts, including walnuts, almonds and pine nuts; sunflower seed, wheat, maize and fresh corn; greenfood and fruit (except orange) are refused by many birds.
Clutch size 1.
Incubation 30 days by female only.
Young in nest About 80 days.

Hand-rearing is usually beset with problems, including infection by the fungus *Candida albicans*.

Yellow-tailed Black Cockatoo *Calyptorhynchus funereus*

German Gelbohr-Rabenkakadu   **Dutch** Zwarte geelstaartkaketoe

Length 65 cm (26 in).
Weight 750–900 g (26–32 oz).
Immatures Like females with duller ear coverts; beak light grey.
Origin South-eastern Australia; taxonomists now consider nominate race confined to south-eastern Queensland and eastern New South Wales, the smaller birds from Tasmania, and southern Victoria to south-east Australia belonging to the sub-species *C. f. xanthanotus*.
Status Common in wet, coastal woodlands.
Aviculture Uncommon in Australia and few breeding successes; very rare outside Australia.

Accommodation 6.
Diet As for Palm Cockatoo (opposite), with addition of peas in the pod, pine cones and, in Australia, banksia and hakia nuts; highly insectivorous while rearing young, consuming 100 to 200 mealworms per day.
Clutch size 1 or 2.
Incubation 29 days by female only.
Young in nest 12–13 weeks.
Sexual dimorphism A male is illustrated; females have brighter-yellow ear coverts and more heavily spotted yellow in tail; eye skin grey in females, pink in males; beak dark grey in males, horn-coloured in females.

White-tailed Black Cockatoo *Calyptorhynchus baudinii*

German Weissohr-Rabenkakadu   **Dutch** Zwarte witstaartkaketoe

Length 65 cm (26 in).
Weight About 700 g (24 oz).
Immatures Like female; cannot be sexed until third year.
Origin Nominate race is from Western Australia, extreme south-western corner (dense forest); *C. b. latirostris*, known as Short-billed or Carnaby's Cockatoo, occurs in south-western Australia (drier forest).
Status Locally common but potentially endangered due to deforestation.
Aviculture Uncommon in Australia, where there is limited but increasing breeding; very rare outside Australia.
Accommodation 6.
Diet As for Yellow-tailed Black Cockatoo (page 63).
Clutch size 1 or 2.
Incubation 29 days by female only.
Young in nest 11 weeks; hand-reared young are weaned between 8 and 10 months.
Sexual dimorphism A female is illustrated; males differ in having dusky white ear coverts and margins to body feathers and in having pink eye skin and dark-grey beak.

Members of this genus must have an endless supply of strong branches for gnawing.

Red-tailed Black Cockatoo *Calyptorhynchus magnificus*

German Banks'-Kakadu   **Dutch** Zwarte roodstaartkaketoe

Length 60 cm (24 in).
Weight About 740 g (26 oz).
Immatures Resemble female but little or no spotting on head in nest feather; heavily spotted by first year; unusually some males have left nest with red tail band; males usually have darker upper mandible.
Origin Australia – widely separated localities in the north, west, central and eastern areas.
Status Common in the north, rare in south-eastern and some areas of south-western Australia; mainly nomadic.
Aviculture Increasingly kept and bred within Australia; rare outside.
Accommodation 6.
Diet As for Palm Cockatoo (page 62).
Clutch size 1 or 2.
Incubation 28 days by female.
Young in nest 11–13 weeks.
Sexual dimorphism Female is illustrated. Male has plain red tail band and no spotting on head.

In Australia some pairs are quite prolific, the record surely being held by the pair belonging to the late R. Lynn. They reared 30 young in 20 years! Hand-reared young are difficult to wean and males are notorious for imprinting on the feeder which may impair their future breeding ability.

Glossy Cockatoo   *Calyptorhynchus lathami*

German Braunkopfkakadu   **Dutch** Lathamkaketoe, Bruine kaketoe

Length 48 cm (19 in).
Weight 425 g (15 oz); newly hatched chicks 15 g ($\frac{1}{2}$ oz).
Immatures Spotted markings on ear coverts, outer-wing coverts and lesser under-wing coverts; barring present on throat, abdomen and coloured parts of tail (also under-tail coverts in some birds); adult plumage attained in third year.
Origin Eastern Australia from central Queensland to eastern Victoria; also Kangaroo Island, South Australia.
Status Locally common where there are casuarina trees, otherwise uncommon.
Aviculture Rare but increasing within Australia; unknown outside.
Accommodation 5.
Diet As for Palm Cockatoo (page 62) casuarina nuts a welcome but not essential addition to the diet.
Clutch size 1.
Incubation 28 or 29 days by the female.
Young in nest 3 months; females sexually mature at only 2 years.
Sexual dimorphism Female's red tail band is crossed with black bars and speckled with yellow; most females have scattered yellow feathers on head and neck; male's head dark brown; tail plain red and black.

Perhaps destined to become the most free-breeding of the Black Cockatoos, this species has a friendly personality and is not aloof like White-tailed and Yellow-tailed. A female is illustrated here.

Gang-Gang Cockatoo *Callocephalon fimbriatum*

German Helmkakadu   **Dutch** Helmkaketoe

Length 35 cm (14 in).
Weight 280 g (10 oz).
Immatures Males with variable amount of red on head, and crest feathers tipped with red; female's head darker grey than adult; young sexable in nest; full adult plumage between 2 and 3 years.
Origin Australia – south-east from eastern New South Wales through southern Victoria to extreme south-eastern South Australia; introduced to Kangaroo Island.
Status Most common in southern New South Wales and eastern Victoria (family groups and small flocks).
Aviculture Uncommon in Australia but increasing breeding; rare outside.
Accommodation 5.
Diet 14.
Clutch size 2.
Incubation Sindel (1989) states 28–30 days, but as short as 25 days is recorded (Low, 1986); male and female incubate.
Young in nest About 8 weeks.
Sexual dimorphism Female has grey head and feathers of underparts margined with red. Male has red head.

Feather-plucking is common in this species – the cause is usually stress.

Roseate (Rose-breasted) Cockatoo or Galah
Eolophus roseicapillus

German Rosakakadu   **Dutch** Rosékaketoe

Length 35 cm (14 in).
Weight 345 g (12 oz).
Immatures Duller throughout with crown and breast tinged with grey; iris brown.
Origin Australia – almost throughout except coastal regions.
Status Common in open country; population explosion this century due to increased agriculture (feeds on crops and grain).
Aviculture Common and inexpensive within Australia, less common and very expensive elsewhere; many pairs are prolific, others do not breed due to obesity (resulting in fatty lipomas).
Accommodation 6.
Diet Greenfood, fruit and limited amount of mixed seeds, dry and sprouted; fresh corn when rearing young.
Clutch size 3 or 4 but up to 6.
Incubation 23 days by male and female.
Young in nest About 7 weeks.
Sexual dimorphism Iris usually dark brown in male and red-brown or red in female.

Eucalyptus or other branches must be provided to allow these cockatoos to line their nest.

Leadbeater's or Major Mitchell's Cockatoo *Cacatua leadbeateri*

German Inkakakadu   **Dutch** Incakaketoe

Length 38 cm (15 in).
Weight 400 g (14 oz); newly hatched chicks 12 g ($\frac{1}{2}$ oz).
Immatures Duller plumage; iris brown, lighter in females from certain pairs; young from some pairs sexable by crest and brighter breast colour on leaving nest.
Origin Interior of Australia, except north, north-east and part of south-east.

Status Locally common, generally uncommon; in pairs or small groups.
Aviculture Common in Australia, less so and very expensive elsewhere; breeding fairly limited but increasing.
Accommodation 5.
Diet 4.
Clutch size Average 3.
Incubation 25 days by male and female.
Young in nest 8 weeks.

The voice of this beautiful cockatoo is extremely unpleasant; it is perhaps the least intelligent of the cockatoos.

Lesser Sulphur-crested Cockatoo *Cacatua sulphurea sulphurea*

German Kleiner Gelbhaubenkakadu   **Dutch** Kleine geelkuifkaketoe

Length 33 cm (13 in).
Weight About 350 g (12 oz); some birds, probably *C. s. parvula*, markedly smaller, especially females, only 30 cm (12 in).
Immatures Iris greyish; beak pinkish-white prior to fledging, gradually becoming light grey, then darker grey.
Origin Indonesia – Sulawesi (Celebes), Lesser Sunda and adjacent islands; introduced to Singapore.
Status Serious decline in most areas due to overtrapping for export.
Aviculture For many years best-known cockatoo outside Australia; less common since early 1980s; limited breeding; a common problem (shared with some other white cockatoos) is the male killing the female if she is not willing to nest.
Accommodation 5.
Diet 4.
Clutch size 2, occasionally 3.
Incubation 28 days by male and female.
Young in nest 10–12 weeks.
Sexual dimorphism Female (illustrated) has red-brown iris, male has black iris.

Citron-crested Cockatoo *Cacatua sulphurea citrinocristata*

German Orangehaubenkakadu   **Dutch** Orangekuifkaketoe

Information as for Lesser
Sulphur-crested Cockatoo (opposite)
except for orange (not yellow) crest and:
Origin Indonesia – island of Sumba,
Lesser Sunda islands.

Status Endangered by overtrapping
and deforestation.
Aviculture Becoming less common;
deserves attention of all serious
breeders.

Greater Sulphur-crested Cockatoo *Cacatua galerita galerita*

German Grosser Gelbhaubenkakadu   **Dutch** Grote geelkuifkaketoe

Length 50 cm (20 in).
Weight About 880 g (31 oz).
Immatures Eye skin pale blue in very young birds; iris brown.
Origin Australia, east and south-east, as far west as south-east South Australia; Tasmania; introduced to New Zealand; *C. g. fitzroyi* (longer crest feathers and pale-blue eye skin) occurs in northern Australia.
Status Local in north and plentiful elsewhere, even on outskirts of some cities; killed as agricultural pest.
Aviculture Common pet in Australia but seldom kept in aviaries due to low value; outside Australia expensive and highly prized, despite being so destructive; it can be difficult to keep them confined.
Accommodation 5.
Diet 4.
Clutch size 2 or 3.
Incubation 26 days by male and female.
Young in nest About 11 weeks.
Sexual dimorphism Iris black in males, black or blackish-brown in females.

This highly intelligent species makes a fascinating aviary subject.

Triton Cockatoo *Cacatua galerita triton*

German Tritonkakadu   **Dutch** Tritonkaketoe

Information as for Greater Sulphur-crested Cockatoo (opposite) except:
Length About 46 cm (18 in).
Weight About 600 g (21 oz).
Origin New Guinea, widespread, including D'Entrecasteau and Louisiade archipelagos; introduced to Ceramlaut and Goramlaut, Indonesia.
Aviculture Fairly common since 1970s; increasing breeding.

Blue-eyed Cockatoo *Cacatua ophthalmica*

German Brillenkakadu   **Dutch** Blauoogkaketoe

Length 50 cm (20 in).
Weight About 700 g (25 oz).
Immatures Like adults but with iris greyish.
Origin Islands of New Britain and New Ireland (Bismarck Archipelago), New Guinea.
Status Described as common in lowland forests in 1970; no commercial trade in this species.
Aviculture Very rare; very limited breeding (USA and Chester Zoo, UK).
Accommodation 5.
Diet 4.
Clutch size 2 or 3.
Incubation 28 days; male and female incubate.
Young in nest About 12 weeks.

Moluccan or Salmon-crested Cockatoo *Cacatua moluccensis*

German Molukkenkakadu   **Dutch** Molukkenkaketoe

Length 52 cm (21 in).
Weight About 850 g (30 oz); newly hatched chicks 20 g ($\frac{2}{3}$ oz).
Immatures Dark grey iris.
Origin Indonesia: southern Moluccas – Ceram, Saparua and Haruku.
Status Rare; nearly trapped out of existence – at least on Ceram – by late 1980s.
Aviculture Fairly common, many being kept as pets in USA and Europe; reduced availability after 1989, when placed on Appendix 1 of CITES; fairly limited breeding.
Accommodation 5.
Diet 4.
Clutch size 2.
Incubation 28 days by male and female.
Young in nest About 15 weeks.
Sexual dimorphism Iris black in male and dark brown in female – can be detected only in very good light, or by torch.

Hand-reared birds are extraordinarily gentle and affectionate, but too demanding of time and affection for most people. As many young as possible should be parent-reared and not sold as pets to assure future in aviculture; hand-reared usually too imprinted to breed.

Umbrella or White-crested Cockatoo *Cacatua alba*

German Weisshaubenkakadu   **Dutch** Witkuifkaketoe

Length 46 cm (18 in).
Weight 440 g (15½ oz); newly hatched chicks 18 g (½ oz).
Immatures Iris brownish-grey.
Origin Indonesia: northern Moluccas – Obi, Batjan, Halmahera, Ternate and Tidore.
Status Large and rapid decline during the 1980s due to overtrapping and habitat destruction.
Aviculture Common; readily available but decreased availability inevitable although one of easiest of cockatoos to breed.
Accommodation 4.
Diet 4.
Clutch size 1 or 2.
Incubation 28 days by male and female.
Young in nest 13–15 weeks.
Sexual dimorphism Iris dark brown in male and reddish-brown in female.

During the 1980s it was, with Goffin's, the most commonly imported and least expensive of cockatoos. Then neglected by breeders, it is now valued.

Red-vented or Philippine Cockatoo *Cacatua haematuropygia*

German Rotsteisskakadu **Dutch** Philippijnse kaketoe

Length 30 cm (12 in).
Weight 300 g (10½ oz); newly hatched chicks weigh 10 g (⅓ oz).
Immatures Iris greyish.
Origin Philippine Islands; south-east Asia, including Sulu Archipelago.
Status Formerly common but rapid decline during 1980s (possibly previously) due to deforestation. Placed on Appendix I of CITES in 1992.

Aviculture Never common, exported in small numbers, limited availability; limited breeding.
Accommodation 4.
Diet 4.
Clutch size 2 or 3.
Incubation 28 days by male and female.
Young in nest About 11 weeks.
Sexual dimorphism Iris dark brown in male and red-brown in female.

It is one of the cockatoos (together with the Lesser Sulphur-crested, page 70) which seems very susceptible to psittacine beak and feather disease.

Goffin's Cockatoo   *Cacatua goffini*

German Goffin's Kakadu   **Dutch** Goffinkaketoe

Length 32 cm (12½ in).
Weight 350 g (12½ oz); newly hatched chicks 10 g (⅓ oz).
Immatures Pinker bases to feathers of lores and head; eye skin pale blue; iris greyish.
Origin Indonesia – Tanimbar Islands in southern Moluccas; introduced to Singapore.
Status Large decline suspected during 1980s due to deforestation and also to excessive trade.
Aviculture Almost unknown until 1972, when commercial export commenced; readily available until late 1980s; limited breeding.
Accommodation 4.
Diet 4.
Clutch size 2.
Incubation 28 days by male and female.
Young in nest 11 weeks.

It is important to establish this delightful little cockatoo; a *horizontal* nest-box or log (either on the ground or hung) may encourage breeding. This species is extremely destructive and attention must be given to making the aviary escape-proof.

Bare-eyed Cockatoo *Cacatua sanguinea*

German Nacktaugenkakadu   **Dutch** Naaktoogkaketoe

Length 40 cm (16 in).
Weight New Guinea birds about 350 g
(12½ oz); Australian about 550 g
(19½ oz).
Immatures Skin surrounding eye pale
blue.
Origin Australia – almost throughout,
except central-western part; isolated
breeding populations, originating from
caged birds, in vicinity of Sydney,
Brisbane, Melbourne and Perth; New
Guinea: central southern part between
Kumbe and lower Fly rivers.
Status Plentiful and increasing
throughout most of its range, which, in
Australia, is expanding.

Aviculture In Australia too common
and inexpensive to be aviary-bred;
elsewhere not uncommon until
Australia ceased to export birds in
1959, then rare until exported from
New Guinea in 1970s; limited
breeding.
Accommodation 4.
Diet 4.
Clutch size 2.
Incubation 26 days for Australian
birds (Sindel, 1989), 23 days for New
Guinea birds both by male and
female.
Young in nest Probably 6–8 weeks.

Slender-billed Cockatoo *Cacatua tenuirostris*

German Langschnabelkakadu   **Dutch** Oostelijke langsnavelkaketoe

Length 40 cm (16 in).
Weight About 600 g (21 oz).
Immatures Less extensive and duller orange-red on throat and lores; upper mandible much shorter.
Origin Australia – small region of south-east from south-eastern South Australia to southern Victoria and south-western New South Wales.
Status Serious decline this century, the population probably reaching its lowest level during the 1960s; it then started to increase and, during the early 1960s, legalized trapping resulted in thousands being sold into the pet trade. They are unsuitable as pets, resulting in many being released and becoming established in areas outside normal range. Sindel (1989) warned: 'If not closely monitored, the current control measures, including legal trapping and illegal poisoning, could see the demise of this species this century.'
Aviculture Lack of incentive in Australia to breed this species; outside Australia rare and only infrequently bred.
Accommodation 5.
Diet 4.
Clutch size 2 or 3, rarely 4.
Incubation 24 or 25 days by male and female.
Young in nest 8 weeks.

Western Long-billed Cockatoo *Cacatua pastinator*

German Westlichlangschnabelkakadu   **Dutch** Westelijke langsnavelkaketoe

Length 42 cm (16½ in).
Weight About 600 g (21 oz); newly hatched chicks 17 g (⅔ oz).
Immatures Upper mandible much shorter; eye skin pale blue.
Origin Australia – two populations in south-western part of Western Australia.
Status Great decline this century but numbers probably now more stable; legally protected.
Aviculture Not common within Australia and limited breeding; rare elsewhere – only successful pair known to author at Loro Parque, Tenerife.
Accommodation 5.
Diet 4.
Clutch size 3–5.
Incubation 23 or 24 days (Sindel, 1989) by male and female; author's experience of new-laid egg in incubator at 36.6°C (98°F) (slightly lower than average) 26 days.
Young in nest 8 weeks.

Perhaps no other parrot combines intelligence and humour to produce such a unique and appealing personality. For the author, hand-rearing young of this species was an entirely enjoyable and totally unforgettable experience.

Ducorp's Cockatoo *Cacatua ducorpsii*

German Salomon-Kakadu   **Dutch** Solomonkaketoe

Length 31 cm (12 in).
Weight 360 g (12½ oz).
Immatures Undescribed, but almost certainly with eye skin pale blue and iris greyish-brown.
Origin Solomon Islands (south-west Pacific, including Bougainville but apparently excluding San Cristobal group).
Status Common in various habitat types, most frequently up to 700 m (2,300 ft).

Aviculture Rare – Solomons have never permitted commercial export of fauna; only one captive breeding known to author (excluding hybrids).
Accommodation 5.
Diet 4.
Clutch size 2 or 3.
Incubation About 26 days by male and female, actual length unrecorded.
Young in nest 9 weeks (1 only).
Sexual dimorphism Iris dark brown in male, reddish-brown in female.

Males are so aggressive it is advisable to cut flight feathers of one wing, and keep pairs in long aviaries so that female can escape from male.

Cockatiel *Nymphicus hollandicus*

German Nymphensittich   **Dutch** Valkparkiet

Length 32 cm (12½ in).
Weight 90 g (3 oz); newly hatched chicks 4–5 g (about ⅙ oz).
Immatures Like female, but with tail shorter; cere pinkish.
Origin Australia – almost throughout, except deserts of Western Australia and Cape York Peninsula.
Status Common in north, more difficult to locate in south, where their movements are migratory; very large flocks occur.
Aviculture Next to the Budgerigar, this is the most popular and widely bred parrot species, with many mutations; low-priced.
Accommodation 3.
Diet 5.
Clutch size 3–8, average 5.
Incubation 19 or 20 days by male and female.
Young in nest 5 weeks.
Sexual dimorphism A female is illustrated; male has face and crest yellow and underside of tail entirely black.

If there is a perfect cage bird, it is surely the Cockatiel. Young birds become excellent pets and many are very good mimics. For breeding there is no better species for the beginner, in pairs or in a colony.

Kea   *Nestor notabilis*

German Kea   **Dutch** Kea

Length 48 cm (19 in).
Weight About 1,000 g (39 oz).
Immatures Crown yellowish-green; cere, eye skin and lower mandible yellow until third year; on fledging, beak shorter than adults'.
Origin New Zealand – South Island from Fiordland north to Nelson and Marlborough provinces.
Status Fairly common in mountains between about 600 m (2,000 ft) and 2,000 m (6,600 ft)
Aviculture Rare; only zoo-bred birds may be exported from New Zealand; outside New Zealand breeding limited but increasing.

Accommodation Aviary at least 5 m square (16 ft sq.); they spend more time on the ground than any other parrot in aviculture, digging and playing – a concrete floor is not recommended. A pool for playing and bathing is essential if these highly intelligent birds are not to become bored.
Diet 4a.
Clutch size 3 or 4.
Incubation 28 days.
Young in nest About 10 weeks but widely differing periods reported.
Sexual dimorphism Upper mandible longer in male.

Famed for their inquisitive and mischievous nature, Keas will even climb on to cars and enter mountain huts.

Kaka *Nestor meridionalis*

German Kaka   **Dutch** Kaka

Length 45 cm (18 in).
Weight About 900 g (32 oz).
Immatures Base of lower mandible said to be yellow.
Origin New Zealand – North and South islands and small offshore islands.
Status Declined due to deforestation and introduction of possums which compete for nest sites; plentiful only on some offshore islands.
Aviculture Rare in New Zealand (found only in the principal zoos); virtually unknown outside New Zealand except for the pair sent to Stuttgart Zoo, Germany, in the early 1980s.
Accommodation Aviary at least 5 m square (16 ft sq).
Diet Seeds, fruits, vegetables, brown bread soaked in nectar, giant mealworms, insect larvae. (This species is brush-tongued and feeds on nectar and pollen.)
Clutch size 3 or 4.
Incubation 28 days.
Young in nest 9 to 10 weeks.
Sexual dimorphism Male's bill longer and more curved.

Pesquet's Parrot   *Psittrichas fulgidus*

German Borstenkopf   **Dutch** Borstelkoppapegaai

Length 50 cm (20 in).
Weight About 700 g (25 oz); newly
hatched chicks 18 g ($\frac{2}{3}$ oz).
Immatures All have a few red
feathers on ear coverts, regardless of
sex; iris greyish-brown.
Origin New Guinea, mountainous
interior from 600 m (2,000 ft) to
1,200 m (4,000 ft) and more rarely up
to 2,000 m (6,600 ft); irregular
distribution.
Status Threatened and vulnerable to
native plume hunters, by whom its
feathers are prized above most others,
except Birds of Paradise; it has already
been extirpated from some areas.
Aviculture Extremely rare until early
1970s, then for nearly 20 years small
numbers were exported; few survived;
limited breeding.
Accommodation 6.
Diet 15
Clutch size 2.
Incubation 29 days.
Young in nest 12 weeks.
Sexual dimorphism Male has a small
patch of red on ear coverts.

A palm log or similar should be provided; excavating this is the stimulus for nesting.

Orange-breasted Fig Parrot
Opopsitta (or Cyclopsitta) gulielmiterti

German Orangebauchzwergpapagei   **Dutch** Oranjeborst-vijgpapegaai

Length 13 cm (5 in).
Weight 45 g (1½ oz).
Immatures Breast green and orange on side of throat.
Origin New Guinea, including western Irian Jaya, but absent from central mountainous area; Salawati (western Papuan islands); Aru Islands (Indonesia).
Status Common in southern part of range in New Guinea; local or scarce elsewhere; up to about 1,000 m (3,300 ft) in forested areas.
Aviculture Rare; no successful captive breeding known to author.
Accommodation 3.
Diet 6.
Clutch size 2.
Incubation Not known, probably about 21 days.
Young in nest Not known, probably about 6 weeks.
Sexual dimorphism Varies according to sub-species. In nominate race male has breast orange and cheeks and ear coverts yellow; female is said to have cheeks yellow, bordered behind by black and below by greenish-blue (Forshaw, 1989); in *O. g. nigrifrons* (illustrated) females in author's care hardly differed (breast perhaps duller orange); in *O. g. amabilis* male has crown black, sides of face and upper breast pale buff and abdomen green, whereas the female is more colourful, having the breast orange, cheeks black and lores pale yellow.

Double-eyed Fig Parrot *Opopsitta (or Cyclopsitta) diophthalma*

German Maskenzwergpapagei   **Dutch** Dubbeloog-vijgpapegaai

Length 14 cm (5½ in).
Weight 48 g (1½ oz); newly hatched
chicks weigh 3 g (about 1/10 oz).
Immatures Like female; adult
plumage acquired at 10–16 months.
Origin New Guinea, almost
throughout, except central
mountainous part; D'Entrecasteaux
and Louisiade archipelagos, Papua
New Guinea; Aru Islands (southern
Moluccas), Indonesia; Australia: Cape
York Peninsula and northernmost
Queensland (*O. d. marshalli*); north-
eastern Queensland (*O. d. macleayana*,
Red-browed Fig Parrot); and south-
eastern Queensland and north-eastern

New South Wales (*O. d. coxeni*).
Status Locally common in forested
areas except *O. d. coxeni*, which is
threatened by deforestation.
Aviculture Not common; a few
available from New Guinea; breeding
limited.
Accommodation 3.
Diet 6.
Clutch size 2.
Incubation 21 days.
Young in nest 27–52 days recorded
for captive birds but about 38 days is
normal.
Sexual dimorphism Female has
cheeks mainly buff, not red.

Nominate race is illustrated; female left, male right.

Desmarest's Fig Parrot *Psittaculirostris desmarestii*

German Desmarest's Keilschwanzpapagei   **Dutch** Desmarest-vijgpapegaai

Length 18 cm (7 in).
Weight 115 g (4 oz).
Immatures Duller plumage, with crown dull yellow.
Origin New Guinea – southern and western areas; western Papuan islands: Salawati, Batanta and Misool.
Status Uncommon or locally common.
Aviculture Almost unknown until mid-1970s, since when occasionally exported; limited breeding – frequent nesting attempts but few successful, probably due to dietary deficiency.
Accommodation 3.
Diet 6.
Clutch size 2.
Incubation 25 days.
Young in nest 8 weeks.
Sexual dimorphism Only in sub-species *P. d. godmani* – male has forehead, crown and back of neck orange-red, merging into golden-yellow on hind neck. Female lacks the yellow on the neck.

Fresh branches or offcuts of wood should be provided regularly for all Fig Parrots as beak may become overgrown, probably because in the wild they have to destroy the fig's woody pericarp to reach fruit.

Edwards' Fig Parrot *Psittaculirostris edwardsii*

German Edwards' Schmuckohrpapagei   **Dutch** Edwards-vijgpapegaai

Length 18 cm (7 in).
Weight 110 g (4 oz).
Immatures Like female, but duller green; cheek feathers yellow mixed with red and shorter; ear coverts greenish-yellow.
Origin New Guinea, north-east from Humboldt Bay, Irian Jaya, east to Huon Gulf, Papua New Guinea.
Status Locally common; occurs in forests and at edges, and partially cleared areas.
Aviculture Almost unknown until mid-1970s, since when occasionally available; limited breeding success due to death of many chicks at a few days (as in all *Psittaculirostris*); varied diet and vitamin and mineral additives seem essential for success.
Accommodation 3.
Diet 6.
Clutch size 2.
Incubation 25 days.
Young in nest 8 weeks.
Sexual dimorphism Male's breast is red, female's yellowish-green.

Salvadori's Fig Parrot *Psittaculirostris salvadorii*

German Salvadori-Schmuckohrpapagei **Dutch** Salvadori-vijgpapegaai

Length 18 cm (7 in).

Weight 115 g (4 oz); newly hatched chicks 4.5 g ($\frac{1}{6}$ oz).

Immatures Resemble female but duller.

Origin New Guinea, north-west from Cyclops Mountains to eastern shore of Geelvink Bay, Irian Jaya.

Status Locally common in limited area, in pairs or trios.

Aviculture Unknown until 1977, when a few reached Europe and USA; since then occasionally available in small numbers; limited breeding.

Accommodation 3.

Diet 6.

Clutch size 2.

Incubation 25 days.

Young in nest 8 weeks.

Sexual dimorphism Female duller yellow on cheeks and throat, bluish-green band on upper breast (male red) and yellow band on underside of flight feathers (male green); female has rust colour on sides of breast.

A successful breeder withheld seed for the first 3 weeks of chick's life; another pair with a chick consumed between 100 and 200 mealworms daily for first 3 weeks of chick's life – consumption then decreased.

Blue-rumped Parrot *Psittinus cyanurus*

German Rotachselpapagei **Dutch** Blauwstuit-edelpapegaai

Length 18 cm (7½ in).
Weight 85 g (3 oz).
Immatures Head green, iris greyish and beak brownish.
Origin South-east Asia and Indonesia, from south-western Thailand and southern Burma, southwards through Malay Peninsula (including Singapore) to Borneo and Sumatra.
Status Locally common, observed in pairs, small groups or flocks – the latter possibly migratory.

Aviculture Occasionally available; rarely bred.
Accommodation 3.
Diet 4, with peanuts and pine nuts, not walnuts.
Clutch size 3–5.
Incubation 26 days.
Young in nest About 6 weeks.
Sexual dimorphism As illustrated – male's head is grey-blue, female's brown; male's upper mandible red, female's black.

Golden-mantled Racket-tailed Parrot *Prioniturus platurus*

German Motmotpapagei **Dutch** Raketstaartpapegaai

Length 28 cm (11 in) including tail but not the shaft bearing the rackets.
Weight Males 225 g (8 oz); females 200 g (7 oz).
Immatures Resemble female but tail lacks rackets.
Origin Indonesia – Sulawesi (Celebes) and nearby islands, also Talaud Islands and Taliabu, Sula Islands.
Status Common in forested areas; in Sulawesi most common at about 1,800 m (6,000 ft); in small groups.
Aviculture Rare; no commercial export has occurred; it was obtained on several occasions during early 1900s for well-known private aviculturists and, more recently, by an American zoological expedition.
Accommodation 4.
Diet 7.
Clutch size Probably 3–5.
Incubation Unknown.
Young in nest Unknown.
Sexual dimorphism Female entirely green above; rackets shorter.

Great-billed Parrot *Tanygnathus megalorhynchos*

German Schwarzschulter-Edelpapagei   **Dutch** Grootsnavel-edelpapegaai

Length 41 cm (16 in).
Weight 260 g (9 oz); newly hatched chicks 13.5 g ($\frac{1}{2}$ oz).
Immatures Less distinctive wing markings with little or no black; iris greyish.
Origin Indonesia; northern, central and southern Moluccas, Tanimbar Islands, Timor, Flores and Sumba in Lesser Sunda Islands, Talaud and Sangir Islands, islands around Sulawesi, western Papuan islands and those off coast of Vogelkop, Irian Jaya.
Status Locally common on small islands or coastal areas, inhabiting primary forest and plantations.
Aviculture Occasionally available during 1980s; rarely bred to date.
Accommodation 5.
Diet 4.
Clutch size 2.
Incubation 28 days.
Young in nest About 9 weeks.
Sexual dimorphism Male has larger beak; 8 sub-species are recognized, with subtle plumage differences, which should not be mistaken for sexual dimorphism.

This beautiful parrot, quiet in manner and normally also in voice (although capable of loud calls) is a highly underrated aviary bird.

Blue-naped Parrot   *Tanygnathus lucionensis*

German Blauscheitel-Edelpapagei   **Dutch** Blaunek-edelpapegaai

Length 31 cm (12 in).
Weight 215 g (7½ oz); newly hatched chicks weigh 10 g (⅓ oz).
Immatures Duller and less distinct coloration – especially on wings, head and nape, the latter with little or no blue; beak is red even before the chick feathers; iris greyish.
Origin Philippines (south-east Asia); islands off north and east coasts of Borneo, and islands north of Sulawesi (Celebes) in Indonesia.
Status Common in forest, secondary growth and cultivated areas.

Aviculture Occasionally available – the small demand has deterred importers; limited breeding.
Accommodation 4.
Diet 4.
Clutch size 2 or 3.
Incubation 25 days.
Young in nest 9 weeks.
Sexual dimorphism Wing markings usually brighter and more clearly defined in male. The delicate tracery is the outstanding feature of their plumage.

Neither this species nor Müller's (page 96) is very vocal; both can be considered ideal for those with close neighbours.

Müller's Parrot *Tanygnathus sumatranus*

German Müller's-Edelpapagei   **Dutch** Müller-edelpapegaai

Length 32 cm (12½ in).
Weight 230 g (8 oz).
Immatures Similar to female but beak pale horn colour with upper central part of upper mandible greyish; by 5 to 6 months, beak is clear horn; iris greyish, changing to whitish at 6 months.
Origin Philippines (south-east Asia); Sulawesi (Celebes) and nearby islands (including Talaud and Sangir) in Indonesia.

Status Common, especially in lowland forest; sometimes occurs in large flocks which damage crops, especially corn.
Aviculture Occasionally imported but little demand; limited breeding.
Accommodation 4.
Diet 4.
Clutch size 2 or 3.
Incubation 25 days.
Young in nest 9 weeks*.
Sexual dimorphism Beak red in male, whitish in female (illustrated).

Unless given more attention by breeders, *Tanygnathus* species will be lost to aviculture.

Eclectus Parrot *Eclectus roratus*

German Rotseitige-Edelpapagei, Halmahera-Edelpapagei
Dutch Rotseitige-edelpapegaai, Halmahera-edelpapegaai

Length 31–37 cm (12–14½ in).
Weight 375–550 g (13–19½ oz); newly hatched chicks 16 g (⅔ oz).
Immatures Plumage like adults (females mainly red, males mainly green) but hidden parts of some feathers in males may be red and conversely some in females green; beak mainly dark brown with lighter brown or yellow-orange towards tip of upper mandible and on lower mandible in some birds; iris greyish; sexual maturity and adult beak colour acquired at about 3 years in male, earlier in some females.
Origin Australia, Cape York; New Guinea, almost throughout except highest mountainous areas; Indonesia: Moluccas (including Amboina, Buru, Ceram), Sumba in Lesser Sunda Islands, Tanimbar, Aru and Kai islands; Admiralty Islands and from Bismarck Archipelago eastwards to Solomon Islands. (*Continued overleaf*) ▷

Eclectus Parrot continued

Status Common in most types of forested areas.

Aviculture Rare until late 1960s, since when regularly available; losses are high among newly imported Eclectus but fortunately demand now supplied almost entirely by aviary-bred birds.

Accommodation 8.

Diet 7.

Clutch size 2, rarely 1.

Incubation 28–30 days.

Young in nest About 11 weeks.

Continuous nesters, females will lay or rear several clutches in succession, breaking up unsuccessful eggs very soon after they are due to hatch. At least 7 sub-species are recognized, only 3 of which are common in aviculture: nominate race, illustrated on page 97, (southern Moluccas), *E. r. vosmaeri*, the Grand Eclectus (northern and central Moluccas), illustrated above, and *E. r. polychloros*, the Red-sided (western Papuan islands, Trobriand Islands, D'Entrecasteaux and Louisiade archipelagos). The female of two sub-species, *E. r. cornelia* (Sumba) and *E. r. riedeli* (Tanimbar Islands), are entirely red; both are very rare in aviculture.

Australian King Parrakeet *Alisterus scapularis*

German Australischer Königssittich   **Dutch** Koningsparkiet

Length 43 cm (17 in).
Weight 230 g (8 oz); newly hatched chicks 10 g ($\frac{1}{3}$ oz).
Immatures Resemble female; beak pale brown; iris brown; adult plumage acquired during the third year but male's beak starts to become pink well before a year.
Origin Eastern Australia from northern Queensland to southern Victoria.
Status Common in forested areas but vulnerable to deforestation and to replacement of native trees by exotic species.
Aviculture For decades a favourite with aviculturists; outside Australia captive-bred for many generations but the fairly high price indicates it is not among the easier species to breed; in Australia aviary-bred for few generations.
Accommodation 4.
Diet 4, without walnuts, plus boiled maize.
Clutch size 3–6, average 4.
Incubation 20 days.
Young in nest 5 weeks.
Sexual dimorphism Male is illustrated. Female differs in having head and nape green, upper breast green tinged with red and remainder of underparts duller red than male.

Green-winged King Parrakeet   *Alisterus chloropterus*

German Gelbschulter-Königssittich   **Dutch** Groenvleugel-koningsparkiet

Length 36 cm (14 in).
Weight 160 g (6 oz).
Immatures In nominate race (eastern New Guinea) and *A. c. callopterus* (central New Guinea) resemble female except in lacking brownish-red margins to throat and breast feathers; beak is brownish-black with paler tip; iris brown. In *A. c. moszkowskii* (northern New Guinea) immatures resemble female but with orange beak (coral red and black in adults).
Origin New Guinea, east of the Weylands Mountains in Irian Jaya.
Status Inconspicuous or not abundant; locally common in rain forest.
Aviculture Rare; occasionally imported but expensive; limited breeding.
Accommodation 5.
Diet 4, without walnuts.
Clutch size 3 or 4 (2 recorded).
Incubation 21 days.
Young in nest Assume 8 weeks.
Sexual dimorphism Female's head is green in *A. c. chloropterus* and *callopterus*, breast feathers dull green edged with red and underparts red (distinguished from Australian King by deeper-blue rump and darker-red underparts). In *A. c. moszkowskii* female shows less dimorphism, having the head red but differing from her male in having less yellowish-green on the wings and less or no blue on hindneck. *A. c. moszkowskii* is illustrated here.

Amboina King Parrakeet *Alisterus amboinensis*

German Amboina-Königssittich   **Dutch** Ambon-koningsparkiet

Length 35 cm (14 in).
Weight 150 g (5½ oz).
Immatures Mantle green (not blue); outer tail feathers tipped pink; eye skin white; beak brownish-black, paler at tip; iris dark brown.
Origin Indonesia: Peleng Island and Sula Islands, eastwards through Moluccan islands to western Papuan islands; western New Guinea.
Status Common in forested areas up to about 1,200 m (4,000 ft).
Aviculture Nominate race (from Amboina and Ceram, southern Moluccas) and *A. a. dorsalis* (western) Papuan islands and north-western New Guinea) occasionally available since early 1970s, more rarely *A. a. buruensis* (from Buru, southern Moluccas) and even more rarely *A. a. hypophonius* from Halmahera, southern Moluccas. Only nominate race established in aviculture – not very securely.
Accommodation 5.
Diet 4, without walnuts.
Clutch size 3.
Incubation 21 days.
Young in nest 8 or 9 weeks.

A nervous species, it lacks the confiding nature of the Australian King (page 99), making it less enjoyable as an aviary subject.

Blue-winged King Parrakeet   *Alisterus amboinensis hypophonius*

German Blauflügel-Königssittich
Dutch Halmahera-koningsparkiet, Blauwvleugel-koningsparkiet

Information as for Amboina King Parrakeet (page 101).
Wild-caught birds have proved difficult to establish.

Crimson-winged Parrakeet (Red-winged Parrot)
Aprosmictus erythropterus

German Rotflügelsittich	**Dutch** Roodvleugelparkiet

Length 32 cm (13½ in).
Weight 135 g (5 oz); newly hatched chicks 8 g (¼ oz).
Immatures Resemble female but with beak yellowish and iris pale brown; males can be sexed at about 18 months by black feathers on back; adult plumage acquired at about 2½ years.
Origin Northern and eastern Australia from Western Australia (Kimberley division), east to Cape York and northern Queensland and southwards to north-eastern South Australia and northern New South Wales; New Guinea, from south-eastern Irian Jaya to south-west Papua New Guinea.

Status Common in open savannah, eucalyptus forests and trees along watercourses.
Aviculture A favourite for decades and bred for many generations outside Australia – but not so free-breeding that price is low.
Accommodation 4.
Diet 4, without walnuts.
Clutch size 3–6.
Incubation 21 days (from about third egg).
Young in nest 5–6 weeks; often double-brooded.
Sexual dimorphism Female lacks black mantle and area of red on wing is greatly reduced.

Timor Crimson-winged Parrakeet *Aprosmictus jonquillaceus*

German Timor Rotflügelsittich   **Dutch** Timor-roodvleugelparkiet

Length 33 cm (13 in).
Weight 130 g (4½ oz).
Immatures Resemble female but lack
yellow in wing coverts; iris pale brown.
Origin Indonesia – Lesser Sunda
Islands – Timor, Roti and Wetar.
Status Fairly common, up to 2,000 m
(6,600 ft)

Aviculture Rare – sporadically
imported and infrequently bred.
Accommodation 4.
Diet 4, without walnuts.
Clutch size 4 or 5.
Incubation 21 days.
Young in nest 5–6 weeks.

Barraband's Parrakeet (Superb Parrot)   *Polytelis swainsonii*

German Schildsittich   **Dutch** Barrabandparkiet

Length 40 cm (16 in).
Weight 140 g (5 oz); newly hatched chicks 5 g ($\frac{1}{6}$ oz).
Immatures Resemble female; iris brown; adult plumage acquired in the second year.
Origin Australia – northern Victoria and interior of New South Wales.
Status Fairly common; observed in small flocks.
Aviculture A long-term favourite, captive-bred outside Australia for many generations but not as free-breeding as *Neophema*, for example.
Accommodation 4.
Diet 5.
Clutch size 4–6.
Incubation 20 days.
Young in nest 5 weeks; sexually mature at 2 years.
Sexual dimorphism Female lacks yellow and red on face and throat; ear coverts are tinged with greenish-grey and blue.

This is an ideal aviary bird with an inoffensive voice.

Rock Pebbler Parrakeet (Regent Parrot)   *Polytelis anthopeplus*

German Bergsittich   **Dutch** Bergparkiet

Length 41 cm (16 in).
Weight 150 g (5 oz); newly hatched chicks 7 g ($\frac{1}{4}$ oz).
Immatures Resemble female but slightly duller; iris brown; males may be yellow on head; adult plumage acquired at about 15 months.
Origin Australia – south-western corner, and south-east from south-western Victoria to eastern South Australia.
Status Abundant in south-west; uncommon in south-east.
Aviculture Outside Australia captive-bred for many generations but among the less common and less free-breeding parrakeets.
Accommodation 6.
Diet 5.
Clutch size 4–6.
Incubation 20 days.
Young in nest 5 weeks; sexually mature at or before 2 years.
Sexual dimorphism Female is olive-yellow where the male (illustrated) is bright yellow (shade varies in individuals); her outer tail feathers margined with pink on underside.

Princess of Wales Parrakeet (Princess Parrot)
Polytelis alexandrae

German Princess-of-Wales-Sittich **Dutch** Prinses van Walesparkiet

Length 45 cm (18 in).
Weight 100 g ($3\frac{1}{2}$ oz).
Immatures Resemble female but duller, especially on rump; iris brownish; head usually larger and flatter in male and crown slightly bluer.
Origin Australia – interior of central and western areas.
Status Rare, nomadic and often elusive, one of the least known of Australian parrots.
Aviculture Fairly common; increased popularity during the 1980s with advent of blue mutation; an unusual example of a naturally rare parrot which is more common in aviaries than in the wild.
Accommodation 5.
Diet 5.
Clutch size 4–6.
Incubation 20 days.
Young in nest 5 weeks.
Sexual dimorphism The female is paler blue on head and greyer blue on rump, with a shorter tail. A male is illustrated: note spatule tip to third primary.

Breeding span up to 20 years; can be bred on colony system.

Pileated Parrakeet (Red-capped Parrot)
Purpureicephalus spurius

German Rotkappensittich   **Dutch** Roodkapparkiet

Length 36 cm (14 in).
Weight 120 g (4½ oz).
Immatures The frontal band is red, the head, back and wings dark green, throat and cheeks greyish and underparts grey-brown. The female's head looks smaller and rounder.
Origin Australia – south-western corner.
Status Fairly common; inhabits *Eucalyptus calophylla* forests, and trees along watercourses, roads and cultivated areas.
Aviculture Not common although bred to many generations outside Australia; limited breeding and availability in UK and USA – more common in Europe.
Accommodation 5.
Diet 5.
Clutch size 4–7.
Incubation 20 days.
Young in nest 5 weeks; sexually mature at about 18 months.
Sexual dimorphism The female is duller, especially on the underparts, which are greyish-mauve. A male is illustrated – but note that the breast colour should be mauve.

Despite its beauty, this parrakeet is not generally popular because of its nervous temperament.

Barnard's Parrakeet (Mallee Ringneck Parrot)
Barnardius barnardi

German Barnardsittich   **Dutch** Barnardparkiet

Length 33 cm (13 in).
Weight 125 g (4½ oz).
Immatures Greyish-green on back and mantle, brownish on crown and nape; stripe on underside of wing; adult plumage acquired between 12 and 18 months; wing-stripe then retained by female.
Origin Australia – interior of the south-east.
Status Common in some areas, declining in others where mallee and open woodland has been destroyed for agricultural purposes.

Aviculture Captive-bred for many generations outside Australia, but not among most popular parrakeets; more readily obtainable in Europe than in UK or USA.
Accommodation 5.
Diet 5.
Clutch size 4–6.
Incubation 20 days.
Young in nest 5 weeks.
Sexual dimorphism Female duller overall, back and mantle greyish-green; wing-stripe usually present.

Cloncurry Parrakeet *Barnardius barnardi macgillivrayi*

German Cloncurrysittich   **Dutch** Cloncurryparkiet

Information as for Barnard's Parrakeet (page 109) except:
Origin Australia – north-western Queensland and adjacent Northern Territory, in the east.
Status Plentiful in large eucalypts growing along watercourses.
Aviculture Rarer than nominate race.

Port Lincoln Parrakeet *Barnardius zonarius*

German Ringsittich   **Dutch** Port Lincolnparkiet

Length 38 cm (15 in).
Weight 150 g (5½ oz).
Immatures Brownish-black head, plumage duller throughout.
Origin Australia: the nominate race occurs in central and southern Australia. Twenty-eight Parrakeet (*B. z. semitorquatus*) is found in the south-west, south of Perth, and *B. z. occidentalis* in Western Australia.
Status Common in various types of habitat, in pairs or small groups.

Aviculture Captive-bred for many generations outside Australia; common in Europe, less so in UK and USA; sometimes double-brooded and quite prolific, but generally not so easy to breed.
Accommodation 5.
Diet 4.
Clutch size 4–6.
Incubation 20 days.
Young in nest 5 weeks.

A male Port Lincoln is illustrated; the female has a brown tinge on the head. Abdomen is yellow in nominate race and green in the Twenty-eight, which has prominent red band on forehead; some Port Lincolns have a little red on forehead.

Green Rosella *Platycercus caledonicus*

German Gelbbauchsittich   **Dutch** Geelbuikrosella

Length 36 cm (14 in).
Weight 135 g (5 oz).
Immatures Duller, head and underparts olive green and upperparts mainly olive-brown with light margins to some of the feathers; some birds have red frontal band; wing-stripe present, adult plumage acquired at about 15 months.
Origin Tasmania and larger islands in Bass Strait, Australia.
Status Common in most types of habitat, even urban.
Aviculture Not common or readily available except in Netherlands and Germany; even in Australia it is the least bred member of the genus.
Accommodation 5.
Diet 4, with seeding grasses, etc., daily.
Clutch size 4 or 5, occasionally 6.
Incubation 20 days.
Young in nest 5 weeks; sexually mature between 1 and 2 years.
Sexual dimorphism Slight – some females have orange-red on throat, most do not have wing-stripe, head and beak usually smaller.

Pennant's Parrakeet (Crimson Rosella) *Platycercus elegans*

German Pennantsittich   **Dutch** Pennantrosella

Length 36 cm (14 in).
Weight 145 g (5 oz).
Immatures In nominate race and in
P. e. melanoptera (sub-species most
heavily marked with black on back),
crown, throat, upper breast and
under-tail coverts are red, underparts
otherwise being greyish-green;
upperparts green. In *P. e. nigrescens*
immatures resemble adults. Adult
plumage is acquired at about 14 months.
Origin Two widely separated regions
of Australia: north-east coast (not Cape
York) is the home of *P. e. nigrescens*;
otherwise north-eastern Queensland to
south-eastern South Australia;
introduced to New Zealand and
Norfolk Island.
Status Except in New Zealand,
common in various habitat types, even
on outskirts of towns.
Aviculture Popular and readily
available; outside Australia
captive-bred for many generations.
Accommodation 4.
Diet 4, with seeding grasses, etc.,
daily.
Clutch size 5–8.
Incubation 20 days.
Young in nest 5 weeks.

A male *P. e. nigrescens* is illustrated; it differs from nominate race in smaller size –
about 32 cm (12½ in) – and darker colour.

Yellow Rosella *Platycercus flaveolus*

German Strohsittich **Dutch** Strogelerosella

Length 33 cm (13 in).
Weight 125 g (4½ oz).
Immatures Mainly dull olive-green and without the dark markings; paler yellow-green below and olive-green on rump; wing-stripe present; in nest feather, though, some young resemble adults.
Origin Australia – interior of the south-east (southern New South Wales, northern Victoria and eastern South Australia).
Status Fairly common near riverine eucalypts and savannah woodland on flood plains.
Aviculture Not common; captive-bred birds occasionally available.
Accommodation 4.
Diet 4, with green food daily.
Clutch size 4 or 5.
Incubation 20 days.
Young in nest 5 weeks.
Sexual dimorphism In the female, throat and breast have more orange-red suffusion, wing-stripe is usually present and head and bill are slightly smaller.

Not as free-breeding as some of the genus.

Adelaide Rosella *Platycercus adelaidae*

German Adelaidesittich   **Dutch** Adelaiderosella

Information as for Pennant's Parrakeet (page 113) except:
Length 35 cm (14 in).
Weight 145 g (5 oz).
Immatures Vary from orange-yellow to dull orange-red on forehead, crown, upper breast and under-tail coverts; underparts olive-green and greyish-green; wing coverts, which are blue in adults, are dull green tinged with blue; upperparts bright olive-green, more yellow on rump and upper-tail coverts.
Origin Australia – a small area from southern South Australia north to Flinders Range; in Mannum area, South Australia, hybridizing occurs with the Yellow Rosella and a transitional form occurs.
Status Common in all habitats with trees, including parks.
Aviculture Not common or popular, perhaps because considered almost in the same light as hybrids but with much duller colours than Pennant's. Some taxonomists classify Adelaide and Yellow Rosellas as sub-species of Pennant's. If it is judged a species, the nominate race is illustrated. The sub-species *P. a. subadelaidae* is more yellow or orange than red.

Red Rosella or Golden-mantled Parrakeet (Eastern Rosella)
Platycercus eximius

German Rosella   **Dutch** Rosella

Length 30 cm (12 in).
Weight 100 g (3½ oz).
Immatures Differ from female in being duller, with nape and hindcrown green; wing-stripe is present but not evident in males after first full moult at about 12 months.
Origin Australia, south-east, and Tasmania; nominate race occurs in south-eastern South Australia, Victoria and south-eastern South Australia; *P. e. cecilae* is from south-eastern Queensland and north-eastern New South Wales; *P. e. diemenensis* occurs only in Tasmania. This species has been introduced to New Zealand (well established in Auckland area).
Status Not common in Tasmania but elsewhere abundant in habitats with trees, including parks and gardens.
Aviculture Most widely kept, inexpensive and free-breeding of genus.
Accommodation 4.
Diet 4.
Clutch size 6 or 7, but up to 9.
Incubation 20 days.
Young in nest 5 weeks; sexually mature at about 1 year.

Regardless of sub-species, in the UK this Rosella is known as Golden-mantled, which, more correctly, should be applied only to *P. e. cecilae* (feathers of its back and wings margined with gold; red darker).

Mealy Rosella (Pale-headed Rosella)
Platycercus adscitus palliceps

German Blasskopfrosella   **Dutch** Bleekkoprosella

Length 30 cm (12 in).
Weight 120 g ($4\frac{1}{2}$ oz).
Immatures Duller, some with red feathers on head, neck and breast; adult plumage acquired at about 15 months.
Origin North-eastern Australia from northern Queensland to north-eastern New South Wales.
Status Common in lowland woodlands, farmland and timbered grasslands.
Aviculture Common in Europe, less so in USA.
Accommodation 5 (not next to other Rosellas).
Diet 4, without walnuts and with green food daily.
Clutch size 4 or 5, but up to 9.
Incubation 20 days.
Young in nest 5 weeks.

Unfortunately, hybridizing in aviaries occurred in the past with the distinctive nominate race, Blue-cheeked Rosella (distinguished by blue cheeks and yellow upper breast), found from Cape York south to north-east New South Wales.

Brown's Parrakeet (Northern Rosella) *Platycercus venustus*

German Schwarzkopfsittich, Brown's Rosella   **Dutch** Brownrosella

Length 28 cm (11 in).
Weight 150 g (3½ oz).
Immatures Duller, back of head greyish with scattered red feathers in some birds; wing-stripe usually present (sometimes retained in adult females); adult plumage acquired at about 14 months.
Origin Northern Australia from Western Australia (Kimberley division to Northern Territory/Queensland border).
Status Generally uncommon but locally common in savannah woodland, coastal forest and even mangroves.
Aviculture Most expensive of Rosellas, not common even in Australian aviculture; limited breeding partly because compatibility between male and female is often a problem.
Accommodation 5.
Diet 4, without walnuts and with green food daily.
Clutch size 2–4.
Incubation 20 days.
Young in nest 5 weeks.

Stanley Parrakeet (Western Rosella) *Platycercus icterotis*

German Stanleysittich **Dutch** Stanleyrosella

Length 25 cm (10 in).
Weight 70 g (2½ oz).
Immatures Red forehead, rest of head green; much less red in plumage, but in males of 4–5 months red areas start to increase; wing-stripe is present; adult plumage acquired at about 15 months.
Origin Australia – south-western region.
Status Common, seen in pairs or small parties in open forest, grassland and cultivated areas.
Aviculture A popular bird, captive-bred for generations, readily available and free-breeding.
Accommodation 4.
Diet 5.
Clutch size 5–8.
Incubation 19 days.
Young in nest 5 weeks.
Sexual dimorphism Male (illustrated) has underparts entirely scarlet; female has underparts green suffused with red, forehead red (head otherwise green) and yellow of cheeks much duller and less extensive.

The smallest of Rosellas, its voice is the most melodious. This is an ideal species for the beginner with parrakeets.

Red-rumped Parrakeet (Red-backed Parrot)
Psephotus haematonotus

German Singsittich   **Dutch** Roodrugparkiet

Length 27 cm (10½ in).
Weight 60 g (2 oz).
Immatures Duller versions of adults, males with some red on rump; wing-stripe present; beak grey in male and yellowish in female; can be sexed in nest.
Origin Australia – interior of the south-east.
Status Common, in fact expanding its range; found where there are seeding grasses, even in urban areas.
Aviculture One of the most common, popular and inexpensive of parrakeets, it nests very readily.
Accommodation 3.
Diet 5, with seeding grasses when available.
Clutch size 4–6.
Incubation 19 days.
Young in nest 4½ weeks; sometimes double-brooded; sexually mature at 1 year.
Sexual dimorphism Male has bright-red rump; female's plumage is much drabber, mainly grey-green above and yellow-green below.

An ideal species for the beginner and for those with limited space or close neighbours; it has a pleasant voice.

Many-coloured Parrakeet (Mulga Parrot) *Psephotus varius*

German Vielfarbensittich   **Dutch** Veelkleurenparkiet

Length 27 cm (10½ in).
Weight 60 g (2 oz).
Immatures Duller than adults, males with a little red on abdomen – can be sexed in nest; wing-stripe present; adult plumage acquired at 12–14 months.
Origin Interior of southern Australia.
Status Fairly common but not numerous; decline in some areas due to habitat destruction; favoured habitats are arid scrublands, mulga and eucalyptus trees on sandy plains and sparsely timbered grasslands.
Aviculture Fairly readily available – captive-bred for generations outside Australia, especially in Europe (rarer in UK and USA).
Accommodation 4.
Diet 5, with daily green food.
Clutch size 4–7.
Incubation 19 days.
Young in nest 4½ weeks; often double-brooded.
Sexual dimorphism Male (illustrated) is more brightly coloured; female has sides of head and breast brownish-green, underparts light green and median wing coverts red (yellow in male).

Yellow-vented Blue-bonnet *Psephotus haematogaster*

German Gelbsteiss-sittich
Dutch Blue-bonnetparkiet (note that English names
are used for the sub-species)

Length 30 cm (12 in).
Weight 90 g ($3\frac{1}{2}$ oz).
Immatures Duller, with smaller red patch on abdomen; wing-stripe present; bill yellowish.
Origin Australia – interior of south and south-east.
Status Fairly common in sparsely timbered areas.
Aviculture Readily available in Europe, rarer in UK and USA; often difficult to breed due to incompatibility.
Accommodation 4 (not near other *Psephotus*).
Diet 5.
Clutch size 4–9, usually 5 or 6.
Incubation 19 days, but as short as 17 has been recorded.
Young in nest 5 weeks.
Sexual dimorphism Males usually brighter on face and redder on abdomen; in *P. h. narethae* female is much duller than male.

The Red-vented (*P. h. haematorrhous*) is distinguished by red vent and under-tail coverts and the rare *P. h. narethae* by smaller size (80 g, 3 oz), greener shade of blue on head (but mauve-blue on cheeks and chin) and brownish-grey foreneck and breast. *P. h. narethae* is illustrated here. The nominate race, the Yellow-vented, has yellow under-tail coverts.

Golden-shouldered Parrakeet
Psephotus chrysopterygius chrysopterygius

German Goldschultersittich   **Dutch** Goudschouderparkiet

Length 26 cm (10 in).
Weight 55 g (2 oz).
Immatures Like female but with shorter tail and yellow beak; males have bluish cheeks; adult plumage is acquired during second year.
Origin Australia – north-east Northern Territory and southern Cape York Peninsula, Queensland.
Status Rare and declining, existing only in scattered populations.
Aviculture Not common in Australia until late 1980s, when a great increase in breeding occurred; outside Australia rare and expensive, although some breeders have consistent success.
Accommodation 4.
Diet 5 plus fresh green peas, seeding grasses, fresh corn and insectivorous food or mealworms when rearing young.
Clutch size 4–7.
Incubation 19 days.
Young in nest 5 weeks.
Sexual dimorphism As illustrated, male more colourful.

Two problems are associated with breeding this species: incompatibility/aggression and female ceasing to brood young after they are 1 week old; nest-boxes with a heat source at side or back to maintain a temperature of at least 21°C (70°F) are therefore used.

Hooded Parrakeet *Psephotus chrysopterygius dissimilis*

German Hoodedsittich   **Dutch** Hooded parkiet

Length 28 cm (11 in).
Weight 55 g (2 oz).
Immatures Resemble female but males usually have turquoise cheeks; wing-stripe is present; beak is yellowish; adult plumage is acquired at about 15 months.
Origin Australia – eastern part of Northern Territory.
Status Uncommon, found in pairs or small groups; numbers declining and range contracting, with fragmentation of populations; probable cause of decline destruction of food sources, such as grasses, through cattle grazing.
Aviculture Not common except in Germany, Switzerland and Netherlands, where it has bred to many generations in some collections; some pairs prove very prolific.
Accommodation 4.
Diet 5 (see under Golden-shouldered Parrakeet, page 123).
Clutch size 4–6.
Incubation 19 days.
Young in nest 5 weeks; sexually mature before 15 months.
Sexual dimorphism Male is illustrated; female is greyish-green on crown and forehead; cheeks and underparts pale green washed with blue; rump and upper-tail coverts emerald green.

Bourke's Parrakeet *Neophema bourkii*

German Bourkesittich   **Dutch** Bourkeparkiet

Length 19 cm (8 in).
Weight 50 g (2 oz).
Immatures Resemble female, with less pink on abdomen, that colour becoming more evident in males at 4 or 5 months (first moult); head larger in males.
Origin Australia – interior of southern and eastern regions.
Status Locally common and, probably due to watering facilities for cattle, even extending its range.
Aviculture Common and free-breeding; captive-bred for generations and inexpensive; inoffensive – can be kept in mixed collection.
Accommodation 3.
Diet 5.
Clutch size 4 or 5.
Incubation 18 or 19 days.
Young in nest 30 days; sexually mature at 1 year.
Sexual dimorphism Female has less pink on underparts, which are marked with buff; blue on forehead usually absent and more white on face.

Blue-winged Grass Parrakeet *Neophema chrysostoma*

German Feinsittich   **Dutch** Blauwvleugelparkiet

Length 23 cm (9 in).
Weight 50 g (2 oz).
Immatures Duller plumage than
female; frontal band small or absent;
upper-wing coverts blue tinged green;
wing-stripe present in females, absent
in some males; beak light
horn-coloured; adult plumage is
acquired at about 9 months.
Origin South-east Australia;
Tasmania, some islands in Bass Strait.
Status Common; in wider variety of
habitats than other *Neophema*.

Aviculture Common in Europe, less
so in UK and USA.
Accommodation 4a.
Diet 5, with seeding grasses.
Clutch size 4–6, more rarely up to 10.
Incubation 18 or 19 days.
Young in nest 30 days.
Sexual dimorphism Blue on wings
duller and greener in female, frontal
band smaller, primaries
blackish-brown (black in male);
wing-stripe indistinct or absent; beak
dark brown (dark grey-black in male).

In breeding condition, plumage becomes brighter in both sexes, this change being
more evident than in other members of genus.

Elegant Grass Parrakeet *Neophema elegans*

German Schmucksittich   **Dutch** Elegantparkiet

Length 23 cm (9 in).
Weight 45 g (1½ oz).
Immatures Duller than female with frontal band small or absent; wing-stripe absent in some birds; adult plumage acquired at 4 months.
Origin Two localities in Australia – extreme western and south-western, and south-eastern regions.
Status Common; increase of numbers and expansion of range in south-west, probably due to land clearance; prefers open country, dunes, saltbush plains and lightly timbered areas.

Aviculture Common since the 1970s; readily available in UK, Europe and Australia; fairly free-breeding; can be kept with finches.
Accommodation 4a.
Diet 5, with seeding grasses.
Clutch size 4 or 5.
Incubation 18 or 19 days.
Young in nest 4½–5 weeks; usually double-brooded.
Sexual dimorphism Female is duller, with narrower frontal band and greenish-yellow abdomen.

Rock Parrakeet   *Neophema petrophila*

German Klippensittich   **Dutch** Rotsparkiet

Length 22 cm (9 in).
Weight 50 g (1½ oz).
Immatures Duller, frontal band usually absent; wing-stripe present; beak light horn-coloured; adult plumage acquired at 5 months.
Origin Australia – coastal areas and offshore islands of the south from Robe, south-eastern Australia west to Cape Lewin, Western Australia.
Status Common in sand dunes and rocky islets.
Aviculture Briefly available in Europe during 1970s but not established; increased popularity and breeding in Australia but not readily available.
Accommodation 4a; large planted aviaries for several pairs have also proved successful.
Diet 5a (note that it is prone to obesity).
Clutch size 4 or 5.
Incubation 18 or 19 days.
Young in nest 4½ weeks; often double-brooded.
Sexual dimorphism Slight – female duller below, frontal band narrower; lores and forepart of cheeks bluish-green (pale blue in male).

Obesity results in low fertility.

Turquoisine Parrakeet (Turquoise Parrot) *Neophema pulchella*

German Schönsittich　　**Dutch** Turquoisine parkiet

Length 21 cm (8½ in).
Weight 40 g (1½ oz).
Immatures Duller than female; most males have faint chestnut patch on wing on leaving nest but some do not develop it until 4 or 5 months, when adult plumage is acquired; young males darker blue on face; bill greyish-white.
Origin South-eastern Australia from south-eastern Queensland to northern Victoria.
Status Increasing after decline during early years of 20th century; not now considered rare or endangered, although distribution is no longer continuous and recolonization has not occurred in north of former range.

Aviculture Extremely popular, free-breeding and inexpensive; captive-bred in many countries since the 1960s; widely available and inexpensive only since 1970s.
Accommodation 4a.
Diet 5.
Clutch size 4–6.
Incubation 18 or 19 days.
Young in nest 4½ weeks; usually double-brooded.
Sexual dimorphism Female is duller, with breast greenish and less blue on face; she lacks red in wing. Orange-breasted phase is illustrated (not a mutation but a naturally occurring colour phase).

Splendid Grass Parrakeet (Scarlet-chested Parrot)
Neophema splendida

German Glanzsittich   **Dutch** Splendid parkiet

Length 21 cm (8½ in).
Weight 40 g (1½ oz).
Immatures Duller than female; males usually have darker and more extensive blue on face than females, with red feathers appearing on breast 2 or 3 months after leaving nest.
Origin Southern Australia, the interior – difficult to define area as sightings are few (probably nomadic).
Status Probably locally common and not as rare as often stated; occasionally large flocks (up to 1,000 birds) have suddenly appeared (mainly in eastern South Australia).
Aviculture Extremely popular, free-breeding and inexpensive (perhaps no other bird of such great beauty can be obtained for a similar price); not widely available until the 1970s; can be kept with finches.
Accommodation 3.
Diet 5.
Clutch size 4–6.
Incubation 18 or 19 days.
Young in nest 4½ weeks.
Sexual dimorphism Female has breast green; distinguished from female Turquoisine (page 129) by more extensive blue on head of slightly lighter shade (also lighter on wings); shade of green is slightly darker.

Swift Parrakeet *Lathamus discolor*

German Schwalbensittich   **Dutch** Swiftparkiet

Length 25 cm (10 in).
Weight 60 g (2 oz).
Immatures Duller, with less red on throat and under-tail coverts; wing-stripe present; iris brown.
Origin South-eastern Australia (south-eastern Queensland, eastern New South Wales to Victoria and South Australia); Tasmania.
Status Winters on mainland, where it is irregularly dispersed, being moderately common in Victoria and scarce elsewhere; breeds in Tasmania.
Aviculture Limited breeding in UK, USA and Australia, more readily available in Europe; melodious voice; can be kept with finches.
Accommodation 4.
Diet 4, without walnuts, plus nectar daily with sponge cake or bread; brush-tongued – note that all-seed diet is injurious.
Clutch size 4–6.
Incubation 20 days.
Young in nest 6 weeks.
Sexual dimorphism Slight – female a little duller; males in breeding condition have red flecks on underparts.

Red-fronted Kakariki (Parrakeet)
Cyanoramphus novaezelandiae

German Ziegensittich   **Dutch** Roodvoorhoofdkakariki

Length 29 cm (11 in).
Weight 100 g (3½ oz).
Immatures Less red on head and shorter tail; iris brown.
Origin New Zealand nominate race – on North Island, South Island, Stewart Island and offshore islands, various sub-species throughout south-west Pacific.
Status Scarce on North Island and South Island, common on Stewart Island, rare on some Pacific islands.
Aviculture Very common, free-breeding and inexpensive; one of the most prolific parrots in aviculture and also an excellent foster parent.
Accommodation 4.
Diet 5, with green food daily.
Clutch size 5–9.
Incubation 19 days.
Young in nest 5–6 weeks; sexually mature at about 6 months.

Females sometimes lay a second clutch before the previous young have left nest; male will usually feed them if transferred to another nest-box. As with Australian parrakeets, regular worming is essential.

Yellow-fronted Kakariki (Parrakeet) *Cyanoramphus auriceps*

German Springsittich **Dutch** Geelvoorhoofdkakariki

Length 26 cm (10 in).
Weight 95 g (3½ oz).
Immatures Duller head colour, shorter tail; iris brown.
Origin New Zealand – North Island, South Island, Stewart Island and other offshore islands.
Status Fairly common to rare in native forest on North Island and South Island, common on Stewart and offshore islands. Sub-species *C. a. forbesi* (larger and brighter) from Mangere and Little Mangere in Chatham Islands is on the verge of extinction; about 20 birds survive on Mangere and 100 on Little Mangere.
Aviculture Common, free-breeding and inexpensive; all captive-bred, they originate from early 1970s importations, prior to which the species was almost unknown in aviculture (the same is true of the Red-fronted Kakariki).
Accommodation 4.
Diet 5, with green food daily.
Clutch size 5–10.
Incubation 19 days.
Young in nest 5–6 weeks.

Delightfully active and inquisitive aviary birds.

Horned Parrakeet   *Eunymphicus cornutus cornutus*

German Hornsittich   **Dutch** Hoornparkiet

Length 33 cm (13 in).
Weight 40 g (5 oz) estimated; newly hatched chicks 6 g ($\frac{1}{5}$ oz).
Immatures Forehead and forecrown black, the feathers tipped with red; face greyish, darker in male; ear coverts pale green and hindneck olive-green; beak horn-coloured; iris brownish; nestlings lack crest; young adults have shorter crests.
Origin New Caledonia in the west Pacific.

Status Decline due to deforestation but apparently in no immediate danger of extinction.
Aviculture Rare, except in Switzerland and Germany, where it is uncommon; has bred well in some collections.
Accommodation 5.
Diet 4, without walnuts.
Clutch size 3 or 4.
Incubation 22 days.
Young in nest 5 weeks.

Beautiful and active, they are seen to advantage in a long aviary, where their swooping flight can be admired. Intelligent and with a great sense of curiosity, they are enchanting aviary birds.

Uvaean Parrakeet *Eunymphicus cornutus uvaeensis*

German Uvaeasittich   **Dutch** Ouvea-hoornparkiet

Length 33 cm (13 in).

Weight 140 g (5 oz) estimated.

Immatures Undescribed but probably with feathers of forehead and forecrown black, tipped with red and face greyish; shorter tail; beak horn-coloured; iris brownish.

Origin Ouvea in Loyalty Islands, south-west Pacific – the island is only 15 km (9½ miles) long and its habitat extends over only 4 or 5 km (2½ or 3 miles).

Status Endangered by destruction of indigenous forest and perhaps by removal of young for local pet trade; a census made in or about 1980 suggested that about 1,000 birds survived – a large population for such a small area which could not be maintained if it was the result of birds being forced into the area by deforestation.

Aviculture Extremely rare.

Accommodation 5.

Diet 4, without walnuts.

Breeding details As for nominate race, Horned Parrakeet.

Red Shining Parrot *Prosopeia tabuensis*

German Glanzflügelsittich (*P. t. splendens*), Taviunisittich *(P. t. taviunensis)*
Dutch Kandavuparkiet *(P. t. splendens)*, Taveuniparkiet *(P. t. taviunensis)*

Length 45 cm (18 in) in *P. t. splendens*, 39 cm (15½ in) in *P. t. taviunensis*.
Weight 280 g (10 oz); newly hatched chicks 13 g (½ oz).
Immatures Eye skin lighter; beak grey and horn-coloured; iris brown, turning orange by 14 weeks; adult appearance acquired by 7 months.
Origin Fiji Islands, Pacific: *splendens* from Kandavu (introduced to Viti Levu) and *taviunensis* from Taveuni and Ngamea.

Status Common to scarce and threatened by habitat destruction.
Aviculture Extremely rare but breeding is occurring; export from Fiji is not permitted; most captive birds are old or captive-bred.
Accommodation 5.
Diet 7; fresh branches should always be available.
Clutch size 1–4.
Incubation 24 or 25 days.
Young in nest 8 weeks.

Unlike other sub-species, *splendens* is scarlet, not maroon, and *taviunensis* is distinguished from other maroon races by its lack of a blue collar. This is the sub-species illustrated – note that beak *is* black in adult birds and illusion of light beak must have been caused by flash units.

Greater Vasa Parrot *Coracopsis vasa*

German Grosser Vasapapagei   **Dutch** Grote vasapapegaai

Length 50 cm (20 in).
Weight About 480 g (17 oz).
Immatures Pale-grey eye skin; beak white tinged with pink.
Origin Madagascar (Malagasy Republic), Indian Ocean, except central highlands; Comoro Islands: Grand Comoro, Moheli and Anjouan.
Status Fairly common throughout lowlands, in savannah, coastal plains, forest and semi-arid areas, but threatened by habitat desctruction.
Aviculture Almost unknown until 1983, when commercial export commenced; fairly readily available but very rarely bred to date.
Accommodation 6.
Diet 7, plus walnuts.
Clutch size 3 or 4.
Incubation 17 days.
Young in nest 7 weeks*.

Females in breeding condition lose crown feathers and skin becomes bright yellow; yellow skin pouch may be evident beneath male's lower mandible. Courtship feeding consists of short jerky movements. In both sexes large sexual organ, which could be mistaken for a prolapse, is protruded.

Active, playful and in some respects pigeon-like, it is a sun-worshipper, often assuming exaggerated postures; behaviourally fascinating.

Lesser Vasa Parrot *Coracopsis nigra*

German Kleiner Vasapapagei   **Dutch** Kleine vasapapegaai

Length 35 cm (14 in).
Weight About 280 g (10 oz).
Immatures Beak white tinged with pink, soon becoming dark grey.
Origin Madagascar (Malagasy Republic), except central highlands; Comoro Islands: Grand Comoro and Anjouan; Seychelles: Praslin Island.
Status Described as common but deforestation has been so severe and widespread that any species which prefers dense forest, as does *nigra*, must have declined and be classified as vulnerable. Population of sub-species

C. n. barklyi on Praslin (11 km, 7 miles long) numbers less than 100 but is protected; no evidence of decline.
Aviculture Almost unknown until 1983, when commercial export commenced; fairly readily available but rarely bred.
Accommodation 5.
Diet 7.
Clutch size 3–5.
Incubation 14 days – shorter than any other parrot.
Young in nest 5–6 weeks.

This is a species for the dedicated and concerned breeder – a highly vulnerable species which will be lost to aviculture unless more interest is shown. It has a melodious whistling song and seems to do best on the colony system.

Grey Parrot *Psittacus erithacus erithacus*

German Graupapagei   **Dutch** Grijze roodstaartpapegaai

Length 33 cm (13 in).
Weight 400 g (14 oz); newly hatched chicks 12–14 g (about ½ oz).
Immatures Tip of tail dark grey; iris grey.
Origin Central and west Africa from west coast east to western Kenya and north-western Tanzania.
Status Fairly common to common locally in lowland forest; usually absent near human habitation.
Aviculture Popular throughout the ages but still exported in excessive numbers with high mortality; not until 1980s were Greys bred in fair numbers but not sufficient to meet demand; some pairs prove prolific, but others never breed, often due to incompatibility.
Accommodation 8, but smaller cages often prove successful.
Diet 8.
Clutch size 3 or 4.
Incubation 28–30 days.
Young in nest 11–12 weeks.
Sexual dimorphism Plumage darker in males.

Greys obtained young make superb pets for those who appreciate their sensitive and intelligent nature; hand-reared birds are very demanding.

Timneh Grey Parrot *Psittacus erithacus timneh*

German Timneh-Graupapagei   **Dutch** Timneh-roodstaartpapegaai

Length 30 cm (12 in).
Weight 320 g (11½ oz); newly hatched chicks weigh 12 g (about ½ oz).
Immatures Like adults but iris dark grey, changing to light grey at about 6 months, and to light yellow by 1 year (as in nominate).
Origin Africa: southern Guinea, Sierra Leone, Liberia and Ivory Coast (western region).

Status Locally common to rare.
Aviculture Imported less frequently than nominate race and less expensive; limited breeding.
Accommodation 8.
Diet 8.
Clutch size 3 or 4.
Incubation 28–30 days.
Young in nest 11–12 weeks.

For pet potential and talking ability Timnehs equal nominate race (Grey Parrot, page 139), universally considered the most talented of all parrot mimics.

Cape Parrot *Poicephalus robustus*

German Kap-Papagei   **Dutch** Kaapse papegaai

Length 32 cm (12½ in).
Weight 320 g (11½ oz); newly hatched chicks weigh 12 g (about ½ oz).
Immatures Nominate race: head, neck greenish to yellowish-brown; body colour dark green/olive; females acquire orange on head from 6 months (Cummings, 1986); in *P. r. fuscicollis* and *suahelicus* all young leave nest with forehead and part of crown orange, which is gradually lost by 6–7 months; sexable at about 9 months, when females regain orange; head remains silver in males; back is darker green than nominate. In the nest, larger size of male's beak is a good guide to sex.
Origin Southern and central Africa; nominate race from extreme south-eastern Africa; *suahelicus* from central-eastern region to south (Tanzania south to Mozambique and west to Namibia); *fuscicollis* occurs in the Gambia and southern Senegal to northern Ghana and Togo.
Status Uncommon, scarce or locally common; declining in many areas.
Aviculture Rare; limited breeding but not difficult to breed.
Accommodation 3.
Diet 8, walnuts greatly favoured.
Clutch size 3–4.
Incubation 28–30 days, even 32 days for first egg.
Young in nest 10–11 weeks.
Sexual dimorphism See under Immatures.

Sub-species *fuscicollis* is illustrated, male left and female right.

Jardine's Parrot   *Poicephalus gulielmi*

German Kongopapagei   **Dutch** Kongopapegaai

Length 28 cm (11 in).
Weight 200 g (7 oz); newly hatched
chicks weigh 10 g ($\frac{1}{3}$ oz).
Immatures Head is dusky-brown
with greenish tinge; plumage lacks
orange; wing markings dark grey and
less well defined; upper mandible
horn-coloured base, grey tip; lower
mandible dark grey; iris greyish.
Origin Central Africa from Liberia,
Ivory Coast and Ghana (*P. g.
fantiensis*), southern Cameroon and
Central African Republic south to
northern Angola (nominate race) and
highlands of southern Kenya and
northern Tanzania (*P. g. massaicus*).
Status Locally common in eastern
part of range, uncommon in west;
inhabits forest up to about 3,500 m
(11,550 ft).
Aviculture Not uncommon; limited
breeding but not difficult to breed.
Accommodation 8.
Diet 8.
Clutch size 3 or 4.
Incubation 28 days.
Young in nest 10–11 weeks.

Hand-reared young make attractive pets; wild-caught adults are not recommended
for this purpose, being very nervous; pleasant voice makes it suitable for apart-
ments.

Brown-headed Parrot *Poicephalus cryptoxanthus*

German Braunkopfpapagei **Dutch** Bruinkoppapegaai

Length 25 cm (9 in).
Weight 125 g (4½ oz).
Immatures Head lighter brown; cere pink; eye skin whitish; iris greyish.
Origin South-eastern Africa: Zimbabwe, Mozambique, South Africa, Malawi, Tanzania and coastal Kenya.
Status Common to uncommon, in forests, mangroves and plantations.
Aviculture Uncommon, occasionally imported but limited breeding.
Accommodation 3.
Diet 8.
Clutch size 2–4.
Incubation 26 days.
Young in nest 11 weeks.

This delightful little parrot is underrated as a pet and aviary bird. Young, especially hand-reared, birds make appealing pets. Its small size and quiet voice make it ideal for apartment-dwellers. The scientific name means 'hidden yellow', because underwing coverts are bright yellow.

Senegal Parrot   *Poicephalus senegalus*

German Mohrenkopfpapagei   **Dutch** Bonte boer, Senegalpapegaai

Length 23 cm (9 in).
Weight 125 g (4½ oz); newly hatched chicks weigh 6 g (⅕ oz).
Immatures Duller plumage; beak pink at base of upper mandible in very young birds, otherwise grey; iris dark grey.
Origin Central-western Africa: nominate race from southern Mauritania and Mali through Senegal and the Gambia to Guinea; *P. s. versteri* (darker above, with abdomen and part of upper breast deep orange) occurs from Ivory Coast, through Ghana, Togo and Dahomey to Nigeria; *P. s. mesotypus* (paler and with abdomen orange) inhabits eastern and north-eastern Nigeria, northern Cameroon and south-western Chad.
Status Very common to fairly common in open woodland and savannah.
Aviculture Very common – one of most frequently imported and, until 1980s, infrequently bred, of all parrots; wild-caught adults too nervous for pets; in USA hand-reared young are offered, but at higher cost.
Accommodation 3.
Diet 8.
Clutch size 3 or 4.
Incubation 27 days.
Young in nest 10 weeks.

Red-bellied Parrot *Poicephalus rufiventris*

German Rotbauchpapagei   **Dutch** Roodbuikpapegaai

Length 22 cm (9 in).
Weigh 125 g (4½ oz); newly hatched chicks weigh 7 g (¼ oz).
Immatures Breast is orange but less intense; orange band on forehead; iris blackish, starting to change colour at 3 months; adult plumage acquired at about 1 year.
Origin Eastern Africa from Ethiopia, Somalia, Kenya and Tanzania.
Status Fairly common and widespread, in pairs or small groups, in arid areas, bushland and near baobab trees.
Aviculture Almost unknown until early 1980s; remains uncommon and, to date, not frequently bred.
Accommodation 7.
Diet 8.
Clutch size 3.
Incubation 24–26 days reported, but 27 days in author's experience.
Young in nest About 10 weeks*.
Sexual dimorphism Male illustrated; female has lower breast and abdomen same colour as the head of the male (reverse of Cape, page 141, and Rüppell's, page 147, in which the female is the more colourful).

Meyer's Parrot *Poicephalus meyeri*

German Goldbugpapagei   **Dutch** Meyerpapegaai

Length 23 cm (9 in).
Weight About 120 g ($4\frac{1}{2}$ oz); newly hatched chicks weigh 5 g ($\frac{1}{6}$ oz).
Immatures Duller plumage, lack yellow markings except on bend of wing; iris greyish; adult plumage acquired at about 1 year.
Origin Central and southern Africa except South Africa.
Status Common or locally common in habitats with trees, especially near water.
Aviculture Common; fairly frequently imported and increasingly bred.
Accommodation 3.
Diet 8.
Clutch size 3 or 4.
Incubation About 26 days.
Young in nest About 9 weeks.

Meyer's (and other African parrots) are often winter nesters and young have to be hand-reared in severe weather. Nominate race (with yellow on crown) is illustrated; 2 of the 6 sub-species recognized lack yellow on crown.

Rüppell's Parrot *Poicephalus rueppellii*

German Rüppell's-Papagei   **Dutch** Rüppellpapegaai

Length 22 cm (9 in).
Weight 115 g (4 oz).
Immatures Resemble female but paler blue on abdomen and with little yellow in plumage (little or none on bend of wing); iris is brownish.
Origin South-west Africa: Angola and Namibia in south-west.
Status Common or locally common, especially where there are large trees.
Aviculture Rare; seldom exported; limited breeding.
Accommodation 3.
Diet 8.
Clutch size 3 or 4.
Incubation Not recorded precisely, but about 27 days.
Young in nest About 9 weeks*.
Sexual dimorphism Male is illustrated; female is more colourful, with lower back, rump, abdomen, upper and under-tail coverts blue.

Several breeders have noted the consumption of live insects (greenfly, mealworms, etc.) while young were being reared.

Madagascar Lovebird *Agapornis cana*

German Grauköpfchen   **Dutch** Agapornis cana

Length 14 cm (5½ in).
Weight 30 g (1 oz).
Immatures Like adult except for dark marks at base of upper mandible; sexable in nest feather.
Origin Madagascar (Malagasy Republic), Indian Ocean; introduced to other islands (e.g. Mahé (Seychelles), Rodriguez and Mauritius), but has not survived or exists only in very small numbers.
Status Common, especially near coast; inhabits brush and cultivation.

Aviculture Common and inexpensive only during eras of importation, then rarer and higher priced because there are few breeders; in UK there exist only 2 or 3 multi-generation breeders.
Accommodation 9.
Diet 9.
Clutch size 5–7.
Incubation 22 or 23 days.
Young in nest 6 weeks.
Sexual dimorphism Female's head is green.

In Europe it is a late nester – in UK, for example, often commencing in August – and this presents problems. The author found that in the warm climate of Canary Islands it nested throughout the year. More nervous than other *Agapornis*, newly imported birds often suffer from air-sac mites, which will cause death if not treated.

Red-faced Lovebird *Agapornis pullaria*

German Orangeköpfchen   **Dutch** Pullaria, Agapornis pullaria

Length 14 cm (5½ in).
Weight 38 g (1⅓ oz).
Immatures Like adults but face orange-yellow and area less extensive; beak brown with black marks near base of upper mandible.
Origin Central Africa (except in east) and western central regions: Guinea, Sierra Leone, Liberia, Ivory Coast, Ghana, Togo, Dahomey, Nigeria and Cameroon, eastwards through Sudan and Ethiopia and south through Uganda and Tanzania to Angola.
Status Uncommon to locally common in lowland secondary forest, savannah woodland and lightly timbered grasslands.
Aviculture Common and inexpensive until late 1960s, since when seldom available; rarely bred.
Accommodation 9.
Diet 9, with soaked seed and figs for newly imported birds.
Clutch size 5.
Incubation 24 days.
Young in nest 7 weeks.
Sexual dimorphism Under-wing coverts black in male, green in female.

In the wild nests in arboreal termitaria; one of the few successful breeders used nest-boxes measuring 25 × 10 × 20 cm (10 × 4 × 8 in), packed with peat, which the birds could excavate; small heat pads beneath box prevented chicks becoming chilled because adults leave nest when alarmed.

Abyssinian or Black-winged Lovebird   *Agapornis taranta*

German Tarantapapagei, Bergpapagei   **Dutch** Taranta, Agapornis taranta

Length 17 cm (6½ in).
Weight 48 g (1¾ oz).
Immatures Young males have black under-wing coverts, otherwise both sexes resemble the female; beak dusky yellow with black markings at base of upper mandible; adult plumage acquired at 4 months.
Origin Ethiopia (Abyssinia), eastern-central Africa.
Status Described as common (in small flocks) in forested mountains, but drought and adverse conditions may have caused recent decline.
Aviculture Seldom imported; reared consistently by only a few.
Accommodation 9.
Diet 9, plus a variety of chopped fruits.
Clutch size 3 or 4.
Incubation 24 days.
Young in nest 7 weeks.
Sexual dimorphism Female lacks red on head; green under-wing coverts (black in male).

One specialist breeder uses deep sloping boxes with base 10 × 12.5 cm (4 × 5 in). Winter breeders – in UK usually start to breed about January; normally single-brooded.

Peach-faced Lovebird *Agapornis roseicollis*

German Rosenköpfchen   **Dutch** Roseicollis, Agapornis roseicollis

Length 15 cm (6 in).
Weight 55 g (2 oz).
Immatures Softer colours; forehead brownish-pink; beak marked with dark grey at base of upper mandible.
Origin South-west Africa: southern Angola and Namibia south to northern Cape Province in South Africa and Botswana.
Status Fairly common in localities near water, in open dry country or mountainous areas, usually in small flocks.
Aviculture Always common, due to its prolificacy; more mutations established than in any other parrot except Budgerigar.
Accommodation 9.
Diet 9.
Clutch size 4–6.
Incubation 23 days.
Young in nest 6 weeks; sexually mature sometimes as early as 4 or 5 months.

A bulky nest is made from fresh twigs so the nest-box should measure 23 × 15 × 17 cm (9 × 6 × 7 in); inspection is difficult. Nesting material (especially bark) is carried into nest tucked into female's rump feathers.

Fischer's Lovebird   *Agapornis fischeri*

German Pfirsichköpfchen   **Dutch** Fischeri, Agapornis fischeri

Length 14 cm (5½ in).
Weight 50 g (2 oz).
Immatures Duller plumage; base of upper mandible blackish.
Origin Central Africa, central region of northern Tanzania only; introduced to coastal Tanzania, coastal Kenya, Nairobi and other districts of Kenya.
Status Common and widespread up to 2,000 m (6,600 ft) in grasslands with scattered trees and in cultivated areas; sometimes in fairly large flocks.
Aviculture Common and free-breeding; several mutations established.
Accommodation 9.
Diet 9.
Clutch size 4–6.
Incubation 23 days.
Young in nest 6 weeks.

This is one of the easiest parrot species to breed, and ideal for beginners. Note that blue rump and upper-tail coverts distinguish it from the rarer Nyasa Lovebird (*Agapornis lilianae*).

Masked Lovebird *Agapornis personata*

German Schwarzköpfchen   **Dutch** Personata, Agapornis personata

Length 15 cm (6 in).
Weight 50 g (2 oz) – unusually for parrots, in most lovebirds females weigh more than males.
Immatures Duller plumage; base of upper mandible blackish.
Origin Central Africa: a small area of northern and central Tanzania; introduced to Dar es Salaam and other areas, also Kenya.
Status Fairly common in well-timbered bush country; hybridization occurs where it is found with Fischer's Lovebirds.
Aviculture Common and prolific; several mutations established.
Accommodation 9.
Diet 9.
Clutch size 4 or 5, but up to 8.
Incubation 23 days.
Young in nest 6 weeks.

Will rear several clutches annually, including during winter, if permitted; in outdoor aviaries, a shelter with electric light, where the nest-box is placed, is recommended.

Black-cheeked Lovebird *Agapornis nigrigenis*

German Russköpfchen   **Dutch** Nigrigenis, Agapornis nigrigenis

Length 14 cm (5½ in).
Weight 50 g (2 oz).
Immatures Duller plumage; base of upper mandible blackish.
Origin South-western Zambia, Africa; sometimes occurs in north-western Zimbabwe, near Victoria Falls. Has the smallest range of any lovebird.
Status Locally common in mopane woodland; possibly declining; inhabits river valleys between 600 m (2,000 ft) and 1,000 m (3,300 ft).
Aviculture Species not discovered until 1904 but frequently imported during early years of 20th century, proving prolific; by second half of century, becoming rare in aviculture; it is established in parts of Europe, especially Scandinavia, but rare in UK.
Accommodation 9.
Diet 9.
Clutch size 4–6.
Incubation 23 days.
Young in nest 6 weeks.

Vernal Hanging Parrot *Loriculus vernalis*

German Frühlingspapageichen   **Dutch** Lentepapegaaitje

Length 13 cm (5 in).
Weight 28 g (1 oz).
Immatures Plumage entirely green; beak pale orange; iris brownish.
Origin Asia: extensive range from India (most of southern half) to Bengal in north-east, and eastern Himalayas from Nepal to Assam, eastwards through Burma to southern China to Cambodia, Vietnam and Thailand, southwards almost to border with Malaysia; Andaman Islands, Bay of Bengal.
Status Common throughout much of range in many types of habitat.
Aviculture Frequently imported; limited breeding.
Accommodation 10.
Diet 10.
Clutch size 3 or 4.
Incubation 20 days.
Young in nest 5 weeks; unlikely to be reared without live food, mealworms, ant pupae, etc.
Sexual dimorphism Slight: female with less blue on throat, or none; eye colour (white or brown) is not indicative of sex.

Philippine Hanging Parrot *Loriculus philippensis*

German Philippinen-Fledermauspapageichen
Dutch Philippijnsehangpapegaai

Length 14 cm ($5\frac{1}{2}$ in).
Weight 36 g ($1\frac{1}{4}$ oz).
Immatures Like female but little or no red on head; beak yellow with black near base.
Origin Philippine Islands (including Sula Archipelago), south-east Asia; 11 sub-species recognized, each from a different island or group of islands.
Status Common on most islands; *L. p. chrysonotus* from Cebu extinct (last recorded in 1929) and *L. p. siquijorensis* from Siquijor probably extinct, both victims of deforestation; more Philippine extinctions predictable.
Aviculture Occasionally exported; limited breeding.
Accommodation 10.
Diet 10.
Clutch size 3 or 4.
Incubation 20 days.
Young in nest 5 weeks.
Sexual dimorphism Female of nominate race lacks red patch on throat and upper breast (as illustrated); head coloration in sexes varies according to sub-species.

Blue-crowned Hanging Parrot *Loriculus galgulus*

German Blaukrönchen   **Dutch** Blaauwkroontje

Length 12 cm (5 in).
Weight 24 g (1 oz).
Immatures Rump red, otherwise mainly dull green with greyish margins to many feathers; beak brownish and dull orange; full adult plumage acquired at 1 year.
Origin South-east Asia: Malaysia, Borneo, Singapore, Sumatra (Indonesia).
Status Common, except in Singapore, in many types of habitat.
Aviculture Often imported; limited breeding.
Accommodation 10.
Diet 10.
Clutch size 3 or 4, rarely 5.
Incubation 20 days.
Young in nest 5 weeks.
Sexual dimorphism Female normally lacks red throat; gold patch on mantle and blue on crown are duller. This is an outstandingly beautiful bird, the quality and brilliance of the plumage being exceptional.

The recommended size for a nest-box is $11 \times 11 \times 15$ cm ($4\frac{1}{2} \times 4\frac{1}{2} \times 6$ in). Several pairs of this and other *Loriculus* can be kept together.

Alexandrine Parrakeet *Psittacula eupatria*

German Grosser Alexandersittich   **Dutch** Grote alexanderparkiet

Length 58 cm (23 in) including tail (in adult male about 36 cm, 14 in long).
Weight 250 g (9 oz).
Immatures Resemble female but with much shorter tail; iris greyish; adult plumage acquired during third (or even second) year.
Origin Entire Indian peninsula: India, Nepal, Pakistan, Bangladesh; also Sri Lanka, Burma, Thailand, Kampuchea, Laos, Vietnam and Andaman Islands (Bay of Bengal).
Status Common in lowlands throughout much of range; recorded up to 1,600 m (5,300 ft) in the Himalayas; declining in Sri Lanka.
Aviculture Regularly imported until 1970; well established and highly valued in Australia, less so elsewhere.
Accommodation 5 (metal and/or welded mesh construction – wood easily destroyed with powerful beak).
Diet 7.
Clutch size 2–4.
Incubation About 24 days.
Young in nest About 7 weeks.
Sexual dimorphism Female lacks neck ring; her tail is slightly shorter.

Very intelligent; a good 'talker' but it is also very noisy. In Europe it nests early (February); breeding span can be as long as 20 years.

African Ringneck Parrakeet *Psittacula krameri krameri*

German Afrikanischer Halsbandsittich   **Dutch** Afrikaanse halsbandparkiet
Kleiner Alexander-Halsbandsittich

Length 37 cm (14½ in).
Weight 105 g (3½ oz).
Immatures Resemble female but much shorter tail; beak orange; iris greyish.
Origin North-central Africa from Senegal and southern Mauritania east to southern Sudan and northern Uganda. Sub-species *P. k. parvirostris* (green cheeks, not yellow-green, less black on upper mandible) is from eastern Sudan, northern Ethiopia, Djibouti and, on occasions, northern Somalia.
Status Common to uncommon in a variety of habitats; widespread.
Aviculture Less common than its Indian counterpart; unlike the Indian, no mutations have been established.
Accommodation 5.
Diet 5, plus sunflower seed.
Clutch size 4 or 5, occasionally 6.
Incubation 23 or 24 days.
Young in nest 7 weeks; usually single-brooded if chicks are reared; sexually mature at 3 years.
Sexual dimorphism The female African (and Indian, normal green, see page 160) lacks black markings but has faint neck ring.

Indian Ringneck Parrakeet *Psittacula krameri manillensis*

German Indischer Halsbandsittich   **Dutch** Indische halsbandparkiet

Information as for African Ringneck (page 159) except:
Length 40 cm (16 in).
Weight 115 g (4 oz).
Immatures Resemble female but with much shorter tail; beak dark pink; iris brown; adult plumage acquired during third year.
Origin Indian peninsula south of about lat. 20°N; Sri Lanka; *P. k. borealis* (light-blue suffusion, greyish-green underparts, beak entirely coral-red or marked with black; lower mandible black in *P. k. manillensis*) is from India, Pakistan, Nepal, Bangladesh and Burma. Feral populations are established in several countries, including Europe and UK. Hardy and adaptable, its ability to colonize foreign lands is equalled only by Quaker Parrakeet.
Status Common in a variety of habitats.
Aviculture Almost certainly known in captivity for over 2,000 years. Perhaps no other parrot has featured so regularly in trade over centuries and at such a low price. It is now established as one of most free-breeding in captivity, with numerous colour mutations.

Slaty-headed Parrakeet *Psittacula himalayana*

German Schwarzkopfedelsittich   **Dutch** Grijskopedelparkiet

Information as for Plum-headed Parrakeet (page 162) except:
Length 40 cm (16 in) – tail accounts for half length.
Weight 100 g ($3\frac{1}{2}$ oz).
Immatures Head tinged grey and hint of salmon colour on lores, otherwise green; beak orange (on leaving nest, almost indistinguishable from Plum-heads); iris greyish; adult plumage acquired by $2\frac{1}{2}$ years. Sexable at 15–18 months or even at first moult (6 months) by black on neck (Smith and Smith 1990).

Origin Nominate race occurs in eastern Afghanistan, northern India, Nepal and Assam. *P. h. finschii* illustrated (head lacks blue tinge, tail tipped with yellow-tinged white, not yellow as in nominate) comes from Assam, Burma, Thailand, Laos, Kampuchea, Vietnam and south-west China.
Status Common (e.g. in Burma) to uncommon (e.g. in northern Thailand) in highlands (forest, scrub and cultivated areas).

Plum-headed Parrakeet *Psittacula cyanocephala*

German Pflaumenkopfsittich   **Dutch** Pruimekopparkiet

Length 33 cm (13 in).
Weight 90 g (3 oz); newly hatched
chicks weigh 5 g ($\frac{1}{6}$ oz).
Immatures Head tinged grey, with
hint of salmon colour on lores and
forehead; plumage otherwise green;
beak orange; iris greyish.
Origin India, Pakistan, Nepal and
Bhutan; Sri Lanka.
Status Widespread in lowlands,
common in some places, now absent
from others; declining in Sri Lanka,
with range contraction inland.
Aviculture Plum-headed was
formerly frequently imported; now
well established through
captive-breeding; Slaty-headed (page
161) imported much less often. Both
are well established in Australia, the
Slaty-headed perhaps more so than
anywhere else. Both are quiet and not
destructive.
Accommodation 4.
Diet 5, plus soaked or sprouted
sunflower seed.
Clutch size 4 or 5.
Incubation 23 or 24 days.
Young in nest 7 weeks.
Sexual dimorphism Female Plum-
headed has head bluish-grey with
pale-yellow collar; shorter tail; no red
wing-patch. Female Slaty-headed has
duller grey head for part of year and
lacks red wing-patch.

Layard's or Emerald-collared Parrakeet *Psittacula calthorpae*

German Blauschwanzedelsittich   **Dutch** Layardparkiet

Length 29 cm (11½ in).
Weight 100 g (3½ oz).
Immatures Rump greyish-blue, otherwise green, with band of brighter green on neck; beak orange; iris greyish; some or all young can be sexed in second year, when beak becomes dusky-pink in male and black in female – head is then pale grey; adult plumage acquired in third year.
Origin Sri Lanka.
Status Decline in numbers and contraction of range in recent years; occurs mainly in forest up to about 2,000 m (6,600 ft).
Aviculture Rare; very limited breeding.
Accommodation 4.
Diet 5.
Clutch size 3 or 4.
Incubation 25 or 26 days.
Young in nest 6 or 7 weeks; sexually mature at 2 years.
Sexual dimorphism Male's beak orange-red, female's black – as illustrated.

It has a more confiding personality than most *Psittacula* and some birds become quite tame.

Derbyan Parrakeet *Psittacula derbiana*

German Chinasittich   **Dutch** Derbyparkiet

Length 50 cm (20 in).
Weight 320 g (11½ oz).
Immatures Nest feather duller, tail shorter; beak red; iris greyish. At partial moult a few months after leaving nest, area between black moustache and green of nape becomes pinkish in females, extending upwards slightly; lilac in males. Beak is then black in both sexes or upper mandible of male is just turning red, from below the cere; iris is white.
Origin North-eastern Assam, India, south-eastern Tibet and south-western China.

Status Believed common, but no recent information.
Aviculture Uncommon; limited but increasing breeding.
Accommodation 5 – too destructive to house in wooden aviaries.
Diet 7.
Clutch size 2–4, usually 3.
Incubation 23 days.
Young in nest 7–8 weeks; sexually mature at 3 years.
Sexual dimorphism A male is illustrated; female has upper mandible black and narrow line of pink on head (see under Immatures).

Moustache Parrakeet *Psittacula alexandri*

German Rosenbrustbartsittich, Bartsittich   **Dutch** Java parkiet

Length 33 cm (13 in).
Weight 110–140 g (4–5 oz).
Immatures Forehead, ear coverts and cheeks grey or brownish-grey, blackish moustache; remainder of plumage green; tail shorter; iris greyish; beak red, changing to black after a few weeks and at about 9 months becoming red again in the male.
Origin Northern India, Nepal, Assam, Burma, southern China; also southern Borneo (possibly introduced), Andaman Islands (Bay of Bengal), Laos, Vietnam and Kampuchea, Thailand, Java and Bali.
Status Common to uncommon in a variety of habitats; declining in Java.

Aviculture Fairly common and free-breeding.
Accommodation 4.
Diet 5, with boiled maize and peanuts.
Clutch size 3 or 4.
Incubation 23 or 24 days.
Young in nest 7 weeks.
Sexual dimorphism In 3 of the 8 sub-species upper mandible is orange-red in male and female; in others it is red in male and black in female. In *P. a. fasciata* and *abbotti* female's breast is pinker, with pink extending upwards as in Derbyan (opposite). A male of either *fasciata* or *abbotti* is illustrated here.

Long-tailed Parrakeet *Psittacula longicauda*

German Langschwanzedelsittich   **Dutch** Langstaartparkiet, Malakkaparkiet

Length 42 cm (17 in).
Weight 125 g (4½ oz).
Immatures Side of head orange-red;
plumage mainly green, darker on
cheeks and crown; tail much shorter;
beak reddish, soon changing to
brownish; iris greyish; after first moult
they resemble females; adult plumage
acquired in third year.
Origin Malay Peninsula, Singapore,
Borneo, Sumatra, Bangka, and
Andaman and Nicobar islands.

Status Common, in groups or flocks,
in forests, plantations and swamps.
Aviculture Rare, mainly because
mortality is high in recently caught
birds and few survive more than 2
years; breeding successes rare.
Accommodation 4.
Diet 7, without chicken bones; seeds
of fresh papaya relished..
Clutch size 2–4 or even 5.
Incubation 23 or 24 days.
Young in nest 7 weeks.

It has a nervous temperament and is susceptible to both stress-related problems and
also filarial worms (present in blood and air sacs).

Hyacinthine Macaw   *Anodorhynchus hyacinthinus*

German Hyazinthara   **Dutch** Hyacinthara

Length 100 cm (40 in).
Weight 1,200–1,450 g (42–50 oz); newly hatched chicks weigh about 25 g (1 oz).
Immatures Shorter tail; eye skin paler yellow; light skin on tongue whitish.
Origin Brazil, south of the Amazon, especially in pantanal region; extreme eastern Bolivia (Santa Cruz); extreme north-eastern Paraguay.
Status Very rapid decline since 1970s due to trapping; 1987 population estimated to be 3,000 birds; almost extinct in Paraguay; inhabits semi-open areas, deciduous woodland, buriti palm swamps; on Appendix 1 of CITES since 1987.
Aviculture Rare until 1970s, when for a decade excessive trapping occurred, seriously endangering this magnificent bird; aviary breeding greatly increased during 1980s.
Accommodation 11.
Diet 11.
Clutch size 2 (rarely 1 or 3).
Incubation 28 days.
Young in nest 14 weeks*; sexual maturity at 4 years recorded in captive-bred birds.

Its beauty and unique personality have made it one of most sought after – and also one of the most abused – of all parrots. Many pairs are kept in appallingly small cages and many pet birds are deprived of a companion. It is irresponsible to hand-rear all young and sell them as pets; parent-rearing and retaining young for breeding must occur if the species is to survive long-term in aviculture.

Lear's Macaw *Anodorhynchus leari*

German Lear's Ara   **Dutch** Learara

Length 75 cm (30 in).
Weight 940 g (33 oz).
Immatures Shorter tail; paler skin surrounding beak and eyes.
Origin Bahia, north-east Brazil, in the Raso da Catarina; undiscovered until 1978; a second population believed to exist.
Status Extremely rare (but not due to human activity); 60 birds known in Raso da Catarina; continued education of local people will be essential for its survival; on Appendix 1 of CITES.

Aviculture Always an extreme rarity; believed to be about 10 outside Brazil in 1990. Only 1 pair has ever bred – at Busch Gardens, Tampa, Florida, where 2 hand-reared young and their father now survive.
Accommodation 11a.
Diet 11.
Clutch size 2 or 3.
Incubation Not recorded but assume 28 days.
Young in nest Not recorded but probably about 13 weeks.

Spix's Macaw   *Cyanopsitta spixii*

German Spix's Blauara   **Dutch** Spixara

Length 55 cm (22 in).
Weight 360 g (12½ oz).
Immatures Shorter tail; bare facial skin light grey; beak dark grey with broad white stripe down middle of upper mandible (present at 1 year in 2 captive-bred young); iris brown.
Origin Interior of north-east Brazil; known with certainty only from Curaçá region, where in 1990 *a single bird survived*; an undiscovered population may yet exist.
Status Apparently a naturally rare species, perhaps due to specialized habitat requirements; small Curaçá population was trapped to effective extinction; on Appendix 1 of CITES.
Aviculture Represented mainly by single, isolated specimens until the 1980s, when trappers took every bird they could obtain. Not until 1986 was the extreme gravity of its status realized. Some private collectors in Europe feared to admit to keeping it and by 1990 this macaw was a major international conservation issue. An amnesty was declared to encourage all owners to come forward to form a consortium; then the captive population was about 20, including 2 breeding pairs.
Accommodation 6.
Diet 12.
Clutch size 2 or 3.
Incubation 26 days.
Young in nest 2 months (Hämmerli, 1991).

Blue and Yellow Macaw   *Ara ararauna*

German Gelbbrustara   **Dutch** Blauwgele ara

Length 86 cm (34 in).
Weight 1,000–1,200 g (35–42 oz)
(females lower weight), newly hatched
chicks weigh about 20 g ($\frac{2}{3}$ oz).
Immatures Shorter tail, full length by
5 months; iris greyish, soon becoming
yellowish-grey.
Origin Panama (Central America) and
South America: northern Colombia,
entire Amazonian region, southern
Venezuela and Guianas, northern
Bolivia and central and north-eastern
Brazil (extinct in coastal south-eastern
Brazil – deforested), south-western
Ecuador, Peru.
Status Common in more remote areas
to uncommon (near human
habitation); no longer occurs in some
areas or great decline due to
overtrapping and deforestation; overall
the most common of large lowland
macaws.
Aviculture Always the most
frequently imported and readily
available of large macaws, also the
easiest to breed; captive-bred young
readily obtainable in Europe and USA.
Accommodation 11.
Diet 11.
Clutch size 2–4.
Incubation 24–25 days.
Young in nest 90–100 days.

Among the most magnificent of birds in aviculture, it seldom receives the apprecia-
tion it deserves, perhaps because it has never been rare.

Blue-throated or Caninde Macaw *Ara glaucogularis*

German Caninde Ara, Blaukehlara   **Dutch** Blauwkeelara

Length 85 cm (34 in).
Weight 750 g (25 oz); newly hatched chicks weigh 18 g ($\frac{1}{3}$ oz).
Immatures Shorter tail, full length by 5 months; iris greyish, gradually becoming yellowish by 1 year; bird illustrated is 18 months old; adults have iris yellow.
Origin Bolivia, in the states of Santa Cruz and Beni.
Status Rare, due to small range – probably never numbered more than a few thousand; from the late 1970s until 1983, several hundred birds exported, causing a severe population decline; no current population estimate; on Appendix 1 of CITES since 1983.
Aviculture Totally unknown until the late 1970s; price was thus high, encouraging trappers; no legal export since 1983 and species remains rare and expensive; breeding increasing, especially in USA.
Accommodation 11.
Diet 11.
Clutch size 2 or 3.
Incubation 26 days*.
Young in nest 13–14 weeks.

Surely one of the loveliest of macaws – the author's favourite!

Military Macaw   *Ara militaris*

German Soldatenara   **Dutch** Soldatenara

Length 70–75 cm (28–30 in).
Weight Approximately 900 g (32 oz);
newly hatched chicks 18–20 g (about
$\frac{2}{3}$ oz).
Immatures Shorter tail on fledging;
iris greyish.
Origin Sub-species *A. m. mexicana* is
from central Mexico (south-eastern
Sonora and south-western Chihuahua
southwards to Tehuantepec and from
southern Nuevo León and southern
Tamaulipas (as far south as Mexico
province); nominate race inhabits
Colombia (as far north as Santa Marta
in the Magdalena valley and extreme
western Venezuela, also Nariño,
southern Colombia), northern Peru
and possibly northern-central

Ecuador; *A. m. boliviana* occurs in
extreme southern Bolivia and northern
Argentina.
Status Common in some areas, rare
and declining in others; possibly
already extinct in southern Ecuador;
favours montane habitat, preferring
limestone cliffs as breeding sites; also
occurs in lowlands.
Aviculture Fairly common in USA,
less so and more expensive elsewhere;
limited but increasing breeding.
Accommodation 11.
Diet 11.
Clutch size 2 or 3.
Incubation 26 days.
Young in nest About 13 weeks but as
little as 81 days recorded.

The bird illustrated is *A. m. mexicana*, which is larger than the nominate race. *A. m. boliviana* is distinguished by reddish-brown throat and reddish bases to ear coverts.

Buffon's Macaw *Ara ambigua*

German Grosser Soldatenara   **Dutch** Buffonara

Length About 85 cm (34 in).
Weight About 1,300 g (45 oz); newly hatched chicks weigh 23 g (nearly 1 oz).
Immatures Shorter tail; iris brownish.
Origin Nominate race occurs in Central America, from south-eastern Honduras through Nicaragua and Costa Rica (Caribbean slope) to Panama (Caribbean and Pacific slopes); Colombia – Choco in north-west; *A. a. guayaquilensis* found in western and south-western Ecuador.

Status Overall decline due to deforestation; already extinct in Canal Zone of Panama; prefers lowlands up to about 1,000 m (3,300 ft); on Appendix 1 of CITES.
Aviculture Always rare; very limited breeding.
Accommodation 11.
Diet 11.
Clutch size 3.
Incubation 26 days*.
Young in nest 12–13 weeks.

Note that Buffon's is larger than the Military, with more massive head and beak; its shade of green is yellower and its tail lighter red. This species is not yet well established in captivity; to safeguard its future, hybridizing with the Military *must* be avoided and existing hybrids not used for breeding.

Scarlet Macaw   *Ara macao*

German Hellroter Ara   **Dutch** Geelvleugelara

Length About 90 cm (36 in).
Weight 900–1,100 g (32–39 oz);
newly hatched chicks weigh about 21 g
($\frac{3}{4}$ oz).
Immatures Shorter tail; on fledging,
lower mandible is grey; iris greyish.
Origin Mexico (Selva Lacandona in
south-eastern Chiapas), Central
America, Panama, northern Colombia,
the Guianas, Brazil in the Orinoco and
Amazon basins, central Brazil to
northern Mato Grosso and
north-eastern Brazil in north-western
Maranhão.
Status Endangered – serious decline
in numbers and contraction in range,
especially in Mexico, Central America

(in Costa Rica, for example, the only
viable population is in Corcovado) and
in Panama; in El Salvador already
extinct; on Appendix 1 of CITES
since 1985.
Aviculture Known for centuries;
imported birds were readily available
until mid-1980s; many bred in
captivity, but not enough; owners of
single birds should consider giving
them a chance to breed.
Accommodation 11.
Diet 11.
Clutch size 2–4.
Incubation 24 or 25 days.
Young in nest About 105 days.

Green-winged Macaw *Ara chloroptera*

German Dunkelroter Ara, Grünflügelara   **Dutch** Groenvleugelara

Length About 90 cm (36 in).
Weight 1,200–1,400 g (42–49 oz); newly hatched chicks weigh 21 g ($\frac{3}{4}$ oz).
Immatures Shorter tail; lower mandible grey and horn-coloured in very young birds but black by 1 year; iris greyish, gradually becoming light yellow.
Origin Eastern Panama and much of tropical South America, from northern Colombia, across Venezuela, the Guianas and most of Amazonia to south-eastern Peru, northern and eastern Bolivia, eastern Paraguay and eastern central Brazil; extinct in south-eastern Brazil and Argentina.
Status Widespread but not numerous; great decline in some areas due to deforestation and trapping; stronghold is undisturbed areas of Amazonia and the Guianas; on Appendix 1 of CITES.
Aviculture Fairly common over a long period; breeding limited (except in USA) but increasing.
Accommodation 11.
Diet 11.
Clutch size 2–4, but usually 3.
Incubation 27 days*.
Young in nest About 100 days.

Beautiful and highly intelligent, it has much to recommend it.

Red-fronted Macaw *Ara rubrogenys*

German Rotohrara   **Dutch** Roodoorara

Length 60 cm (24 in).
Weight About 525 g (19 oz).
Immatures Brownish-red forehead and red ear coverts; pale orange on abdomen; red feathers on forehead appear at 6–12 months; iris greyish.
Origin Bolivia – southern-central region in south-east Cochabamba, western Santa Cruz, northern Chuquisaca and eastern Potosí.
Status The extensive trapping which occurred between 1973 and 1983 caused a serious decline because the range is small (approximately 160 sq. km, 62 sq. miles); hopefully there has been some recovery; in 1984 Bolivia implemented a ban on the export of birds and in 1983 *rubrogenys* was placed on Appendix 1 of CITES.
Aviculture Totally unknown until 1973; at first small numbers exported, but these gradually increased; in 1980 811 were imported to USA, a scandalously high proportion of population – estimated at between 3,000 and 5,000 a year later. It remains uncommon but is breeding prolifically in some aviaries. Unusually, there is an excess of females.
Accommodation 11.
Diet 11.
Clutch size 3.
Incubation 26 days.
Young in nest 12 weeks*.

Yellow-collared Macaw *Ara auricollis*

German Goldnackenara   **Dutch** Geelnekara

Length 40 cm (16 in).
Weight 250 g (9 oz); newly hatched chicks weigh 12 g (about ½ oz).
Immatures Whitish culmen (ridge of upper mandible); feet and iris greyish.
Origin Northern and eastern Bolivia, eastwards into Brazil to Mato Grosso and southwards into northern Paraguay (Jujuy and Salta) and north-western Argentina.
Status Common in a variety of habitats, including agricultural areas.

Aviculture Almost unknown until early 1970s; now common and frequently bred in USA; less so elsewhere, although prolific and ideal for beginner.
Accommodation 12.
Diet 6, plus walnuts and fresh vegetables.
Clutch size 3 or 4.
Incubation 24–26 days.
Young in nest 10 weeks.

Apart from loud voice, it makes a good pet, being inquisitive, mischievous and a good mimic. Hand-reared birds will try to dominate the household!

Severe or Chestnut-fronted Macaw   *Ara severa*

German Rotbugara   **Dutch** Severa-ara

Length 49 cm (19 in).
Weight About 360 g (13 oz).
Immatures Plumage like adults; iris greyish.
Origin Panama and a large range over northern part of South America: Colombia, Venezuela, Guyana, Surinam, French Guiana, north-eastern Brazil, eastern Peru, northern Bolivia and Ecuador.
Status Said to be common in varzea (seasonally flooded) forest and at forest edges throughout much of its range; decline in Panama and western Ecuador due to deforestation. If it was common over such a larger area, it is surprising that it has, over the years, only been exported in large numbers from Bolivia.
Aviculture Uncommon except in USA, where thousands were imported from Bolivia during late 1970s and early 1980s; little interest shown in this species until the late 1980s; breeding limited but increasing.
Accommodation 12.
Diet 8, plus walnuts and a variety of fresh vegetables.
Clutch size Usually 3, sometimes 2.
Incubation 24–26 days.
Young in nest 12 weeks.

Red-bellied Macaw   *Ara manilata*

German Rotbauchara   **Dutch** Roodbuikara

Length 46 cm (18 in).
Weight 300 g ($10\frac{1}{2}$ oz); newly hatched chicks weigh 13 g (about $\frac{1}{2}$ oz).
Immatures Head only tinged with blue; facial skin whitish-yellow (yellow in adults); upper mandible white on culmen, lower mandible light and dark grey.
Origin North-eastern Colombia, eastern Venezuela and Guianas, south to north-eastern and central Brazil and northern Bolivia, Trinidad.
Status Locally common in humid lowlands with buriti palms (*Mauritia flexiosa*).
Aviculture Rare until late 1970s, then regularly offered in small numbers; mortality rate is high in imported birds; remains uncommon and rarely bred.
Accommodation 12.
Diet 4, emphasis on fruits and vegetables; palm fruits if available.
Clutch size 3 or 4.
Incubation 25 days.
Young in nest 11 weeks*.

Prone to obesity, it should be encouraged to fly by placing perches only at ends of enclosures; cases of sudden death often due to atherosclerosis and fatty and degenerative changes in the heart. It has a nervous temperament and does not readily adapt to confinement.

Illiger's Macaw   *Ara maracana*

German Marakana, Rotrückenara   **Dutch** Illigerara

Length 41 cm (16 in).
Weight 265 g (9½ oz); newly hatched chicks weigh 11 g (about ½ oz).
Immatures Facial skin yellower; iris dark brown, soon changing to reddish-brown.
Origin Eastern Brazil, from southern Pará and Maranhão south to coastal region (formerly from southern Bahia to Rio Grande do Sul); eastern Paraguay and north-eastern Argentina (Misiones).
Status Declining; rare in parts of range but little information; perhaps almost extinct in Paraguay, Argentina and south-eastern Brazil; on Appendix 1 of CITES since 1989.
Aviculture Uncommon; most birds available are captive-bred; it is prolific and captive population should increase greatly during 1990s.
Accommodation 11.
Diet 11.
Clutch size 3 or 4.
Incubation Usually 23 for last egg but author has recorded 24–27 days for other eggs, and once 28 days for last egg.
Young in nest 8–10 weeks.

Hahn's Macaw   *Ara (or Diopsittaca) nobilis nobilis*

German Hahn's Zwergara   **Dutch** Hahnara

Length 31 cm (12 in).
Weight 165 g (6 oz).
Immatures Bend of wing and carpal edge green, only under-wing coverts red; feathers of forehead broadly margined with dark grey, margins narrower on crown; iris greyish-brown.
Origin Venezuela (eastern region), Guyana, probably also French Guiana, north-eastern Brazil – Roraima, northern Pará and Amapá.

Status Common or locally common, usually in semi-open lowland areas, even on outskirts of cities, such as Georgetown, Guyana.
Aviculture Fairly common; regularly exported from Guyana; free-breeding.
Accommodation 11.
Diet 11 (large nuts must be cracked).
Clutch size 2–5, usually 4.
Incubation 24 days.
Young in nest 8 weeks.

Hand-reared young make excellent pets, allowing for the harsh voice.

Noble Macaw   *Ara (*or *Diopsittaca) nobilis cumanensis*

German Lichtenstein's Zwergara   **Dutch** Lichtensteinara

Length 35 cm (14 in).
Weight 190 g (6½ oz).
Immatures Less blue on head; no red at bend of wing; facial skin greyish.
Origin Interior of Brazil, extreme south-eastern Peru and northern Bolivia.
Status Locally common, probably stable population.

Aviculture Now uncommon as export has ceased; limited breeding but easy to breed.
Accommodation 11.
Diet 11 (large nuts must be cracked).
Clutch size 2–4.
Incubation 24 days.
Young in nest 8 weeks.

In some respects this species is nearer to *Aratinga* conures and is perhaps more correctly classified in the monotypical (containing 1 species) genus *Diopsittaca*. Its small size, more rapid development of young, pronounced immature plumage (as in *Aratinga* species with red on head) and its habit of assembling in flocks are all reminiscent of that genus.

Queen of Bavaria's or Golden Conure
*Aratinga (*or *Guaruba) guarouba*

German Goldsittich   **Dutch** Goudparkiet

Length 38 cm (15 in).
Weight 270 g (9½ oz).
Immatures More green in plumage, especially on wing coverts, also on cheeks, crown and tail; underparts lightly marked with dull green.
Origin North-east Brazil, south of the Amazon, in eastern Pará and adjacent and northern Maranhão, to western side of Tapajós.
Status Rare or uncommon in lowland rain forest; declining due to deforestation, construction of highways, human colonization, trapping, destruction of nest sites, construction of Tucurui dam and flooding of 2,300 sq. km (888 sq. miles).
Aviculture Always rare and expensive; captive breeding increasing and very successful in some collections.
Accommodation 8.
Diet 8.
Clutch size 3.
Incubation 26 days.
Young in nest 10 weeks.

In spite of its unpleasant voice, its intelligence and appeal mean that in USA young are hand-reared for pets, not used for breeding, which is highly regrettable in an endangered species.

Sharp-tailed Conure   *Aratinga acuticaudata acuticaudata*

German Spitzschwanzsittich   **Dutch** Spitzstaartaratinga

Length 36 cm (14 in).
Weight 165 g (6 oz).
Immatures Blue confined to forehead; iris greyish.
Origin Brazil (south-western Mato Grosso, southern Brazil) to eastern Bolivia, western Uruguay and Argentina; *A. a. neumanni* (top of head blue, sides green, underparts tinged blue) is from southern Bolivia (at about 2,000 m, 6,600 ft); *A. a. haemorrhous* (Blue-crowned Conure) is widely separated, from north-eastern Colombia, island of Margarita and interior of north-eastern Brazil (blue only on forehead and forecrown, lower mandible horn-coloured).
Status Common in open habitats, sometimes in large flocks; rare in western Uruguay.
Aviculture Common in USA, less so elsewhere.
Accommodation 8.
Diet 8.
Clutch size 3.
Incubation 23 or 24 days.
Young in nest 7–8 weeks.

Hand-reared birds make extremely attractive and intelligent pets (comparable to small macaws) if the loud voice can be overlooked.

Red-throated Conure   *Aratinga holochlora rubritorquis*

German Guatemalasittich   **Dutch** Roodkeelaratinga

Length 30 cm (12 in).
Weight 130 g (4½ oz).
Immatures Plumage entirely green; iris greyish.
Origin Central America: Guatemala and El Salvador to northern Nicaragua; nominate race is found in eastern and southern Mexico; *A. h. brevipes* occurs only on Socorro Island, off west coast of Mexico; *A. h. brewsteri* is from north-western Mexico; and *A. h. strenua* from Pacific slopes of Central America from Oaxaca, Mexico, south to northern Nicaragua.
Status *A. h. rubritorquis* is common in highland pine forests; throughout most of its range, it is a common inhabitant of lowlands and lower highlands in deciduous forest, scrub and clearings, except on Socorro Island, where it is very rare.
Aviculture *A. h. rubritorquis* was unknown until the late 1970s and remains rare; other races seldom available, probably because there is no demand for an all-green *Aratinga*; limited breeding.
Accommodation 7 or 8.
Diet 7.
Clutch size 3 or 4.
Incubation 24–25 days.
Young in nest 8 weeks.

Only *A. h. rubritorquis* (illustrated here) is colourful; the other sub-species are known as the Green Conure, having no other colours except occasionally a few spots of red on the head.

Finsch's Conure *Aratinga finschi*

German Finschsittich   **Dutch** Finscharatinga

Length 28 cm (11 in).
Weight 135–175 g (5–6½ oz).
Immatures Little or no red on forehead and less red on bend of wing; iris greyish.
Origin Central America: southern Nicaragua, Costa Rica (except most of the west) and western Panama.
Status Locally common and nomadic, in foothills and lower slopes of highlands in semi–open areas or secondary growth.
Aviculture Fairly well known in the USA, less so elsewhere; limited breeding.
Accommodation 7 or 8.
Diet 7.
Clutch size 3 or 4.
Incubation 23 days.
Young in nest 8 weeks.

The harsh voice of this and all other *Aratinga* is the main reason for their lack of popularity. Apart from this, hand-reared birds make attractive pets.

Wagler's Conure *Aratinga wagleri*

German Kolumbiasittich, Perusittich *(A. w. frontata)*
Dutch Peruparkiet *(A. w. frontata)*

Length 36 cm (14 in) *A. w. frontata* 40 cm (16 in).
Weight 180–260 g (6$\frac{1}{2}$–9 oz); newly hatched chicks of *A. w. frontata* weight 10 g ($\frac{1}{3}$ oz).
Immatures Red on head duller and less extensive or absent; eye skin less striking white; iris greyish; in very young birds soft pads on upper mandible are black.
Origin Nominate race (red on forehead not extending to eyes and lores) is from northern and western Colombia and north-western Venezuela; *A. w. frontata* (illustrated) from western Ecuador and western Peru; *A. w. transilis* (darker green than nominate) is from northern Venezuela and eastern Colombia; *A. w. minor* (smaller, more red on thighs, feet grey, not pinkish) occurs in central and southern Peru.
Status Locally abundant in vicinity of cliff faces for roosting and breeding; inhabit Andean slopes between 500 m (1,650 ft) and 2,000 m (6,600 ft).
Aviculture Rare to uncommon; very limited breeding – *A. w. frontata* should soon be established in Denmark.
Accommodation 8.
Diet 7.
Clutch size 3 or 4.
Incubation 23 days.
Young in nest 8–9 weeks.

Intelligent but noisy, hand-reared birds make charming pets.

Mitred Conure   *Aratinga mitrata*

German Rotmaskensittich   **Dutch** Roodmaskeraratinga

Length 38 cm (15 in).
Weight 200 g (7 oz); newly hatched chicks weigh 11 g (nearly ½ oz).
Immatures Red on head is darker and confined to forehead – or with one or two red feathers on head; iris brown.
Origin Central and southern Peru, through eastern Bolivia to north-western Argentina.
Status Locally common in woodlands between 1,000 m (3,300 ft) and 2,500 m (8,250 ft).
Aviculture Since mid-1970s common in USA, slightly less so elsewhere; limited breeding yet not difficult to breed.
Accommodation 7.
Diet 7.
Clutch size 3.
Incubation 23 days.
Young in nest 9 weeks*.

Like other *Aratinga* with red on head, they are usually single-brooded, even if chicks are removed; hand-reared young make excellent and playful (though usually noisy!) pets.

Red-masked Conure *Aratinga erythrogenys*

German Guayaquilsittich   **Dutch** Guayaquilparkiet

Length 33 cm (13 in).
Weight 200 g (7 oz).
Immatures Narrow line of brown above cere – no red on head; under-wing coverts red; at about 6 months, when red-flecked feathers appear on head, they are difficult to distinguish from the Mitred Conure (*A. mitrata*); however, eye skin is yellowish in young *A. erythrogenys* (yellow in adults) and white in *A. mitrata* at all ages.
Origin Western Ecuador, arid zone, and north-western Peru.

Status Locally common but a decline noted in some areas; occurs in various types of lowland habitat.
Aviculture Occasionally imported; limited breeding.
Accommodation 7 or 8.
Diet 7.
Clutch size 3 or 4.
Incubation 24 days.
Young in nest About 57 days but between 7 and 9 weeks recorded; usually nest in late summer in Europe, laying in July.

White-eyed Conure *Aratinga leucophthalmus*

German Pavuasittich   **Dutch** Witoogaratinga

Length 32 cm (12½ in).
Weight 140 g (5 oz).
Immatures Bend of wing
yellowish-green, lesser under-wing
coverts green tinged with red and
greater under-wing coverts olive; iris
brownish; isolated red feathers on head
and neck absent.
Origin Tropical South America east
of the Andes, from Venezuela, eastern
Colombia and the Guianas, through
Brazil to Peru, Bolivia, Paraguay,
northern Argentina and northern

Uruguay; its range is more extensive
than any other member of the genus.
Status Common or locally common,
especially in lowland areas.
Aviculture Imported only in small
numbers, probably because there is no
demand; limited breeding.
Accommodation 8.
Diet 7.
Clutch size Usually 4.
Incubation Probably 24 days but no
precise published information.
Young in nest 9 weeks.

Hispaniolan Conure *Aratinga chloroptera*

German Haitisittich   **Dutch** Hispaniolaparkiet

Length 32 cm (12½ in).
Weight 150 g (5½ oz); newly hatched
chicks weigh 9 g (⅓ oz).
Immatures Red on under-wing
coverts and bend of wing limited to a
few flecks; inconspicuous grey marks
on sides of upper mandible.
Origin Haiti and Dominican Republic
(which form island of Hispaniola).
Status Locally common in Dominican
Republic in various types of habitat
but especially mountain forest; rarer in
Haiti, where much deforestation

has occurred.
Aviculture Rare; kept in very few
collections, therefore limited breeding
but not difficult to breed.
Accommodation 7 or 8.
Diet 7.
Clutch size 2–4.
Incubation 26 days (27 for first egg –
consistent results from a pair at
Palmitos Park – a longer period than
for other *Aratinga*).
Young in nest Usually 55–58 days.

Cuban Conure *Aratinga euops*

German Kubasittich   **Dutch** Cubaparkiet

Length 26 cm (10 in).
Weight 90 g (3 oz).
Immatures Carpal edge of wing green, less red on under-wing coverts; iris brown, becoming lighter by 4 months.
Origin Island of Cuba.
Status Locally common in heavily forested areas but declining overall; extinct on Isle of Pines since early 20th century.
Aviculture Rare, except in Germany; breeding increasing.
Accommodation 7.
Diet 7.
Clutch size 4 or 5.
Incubation 23–26 days recorded.
Young in nest 48–60 days.

Egg-breaking is often a problem with this conure; eggs may have to be fostered or artificially incubated, or a nest-box constructed, to thwart egg-breakers; use concave base with hole in centre, beneath which is a false bottom lined with wood shavings.

Golden-capped Conure *Aratinga auricapilla*

German Goldkappensittich   **Dutch** Goudkaparatinga

Length 30 cm (12 in).
Weight 145 g (5 oz).
Immatures Head markings duller, yellow less extensive and cheeks greener; less red on underparts; little or no red margins to rump feathers and those of lower back; iris brownish; eye skin much whiter.
Origin North-eastern Brazil, northern Bahia; *A. a. aurifrons* (greener on head and upper breast, rump and back feathers lack red margins) is from south-eastern Brazil (Minas Gerais and southern Goiás south to Santa Catarina).
Status Rare and declining, especially in south-east, due to deforestation; dependent on forest.
Aviculture Rare until early 1970s, when small numbers reached Europe and USA; often prolific, it was quickly established in USA, partly because hand-reared birds were popular as pets; it is less well established in Europe.
Accommodation 7 or 8.
Diet 7.
Clutch size 3–5.
Incubation 25 days.
Young in nest 7–8 weeks; if young are removed, they may nest 2 or 3 times annually. Sexually mature at 2–3 years.

This species, Jendaya and Sun Conures are treated as either distinct species or conspecific (belonging to the same species).

Jendaya Conure *Aratinga jandaya*

German Jendayasittich   **Dutch** Jendayaparkiet

Length 30 cm (12 in).
Weight 120 g (4½ oz).
Immatures Plumage variable but generally yellower on head and underparts, some feathers green or marked with green; eye skin white.
Origin North-east Brazil from Pará and northern Goiás east to Alagoas, Pernambuco and Ceará.
Status Locally common in small numbers; increasing and spreading north-west due to tolerance of habitat disturbance and colonizing deforested areas.
Aviculture Formerly common, now varies from fairly common in USA to uncommon elsewhere, likewise breeding successes.
Accommodation 7 or 8.
Diet 8.
Clutch size 3–6, usually 4.
Incubation 25 days but as short as 23 recorded.
Young in nest 8–9 weeks.

See note page 193.

Sun Conure   *Aratinga solstitialis*

German Sonnensittich   **Dutch** Zonparkiet

Length 30 cm (12 in).
Weight 120 g (4 oz).
Immatures Plumage variable, but some show little orange, underparts being mainly greenish-yellow and upper back and scapulars mainly green; cere white; eye skin whiter than in adults; adult plumage acquired at about 2 years.
Origin South-eastern Venezuela, southern Guianas, north-eastern Brazil, mainly north of the Amazon.
Status Local in scrubland and savannah, usually in small groups.

Aviculture Almost unknown until 1971, when importation into Europe and USA from Guyana commenced; fairly free-breeding; mainly captive-bred birds available.
Accommodation 7 or 8.
Diet 7.
Clutch size 3 or 4.
Incubation 24 or 25 days.
Young in nest 7–8 weeks; newly hatched chicks have yellowish down, whereas in *A. auricapilla* and *A. jandaya* this is white.

See note page 193. As with the Jendaya Conure, the harsh voice is a disadvantage.

Weddell's or Dusky-headed Conure   *Aratinga weddellii*

German Braunkopfsittich   **Dutch** Weddellaratinga

Length 28 cm (11 in).
Weight 95 g ($3\frac{1}{4}$ oz).
Immatures Head colour slightly
duller; sides of upper mandible pink,
fairly quickly becoming black; cere
white; iris brown.
Origin South-eastern Colombia,
eastern Peru and north-western Brazil
to north-eastern Bolivia.
Status Common along edges of rivers
and forests, especially in the lowlands.
Aviculture Almost unknown until
mid-1970s, since when occasionally
imported but remains uncommon;
limited breeding except in USA.
Accommodation 7.
Diet 7.
Clutch size 3 or 4.
Incubation 25 days.
Young in nest 8 or 9 weeks.

This is perhaps the least noisy of the genus. Hand-reared young make playful and
affectionate pets.

Jamaican Conure *Aratinga nana nana*

German Jamaikasittich   **Dutch** Jamaicaparkiet

Length 26 cm (10 in).
Weight 90 g (3 oz).
Immatures Slightly duller; iris brown.
Origin Jamaica; sub-species *A. n. astec*
(about 2 cm ($\frac{3}{4}$ in) smaller and yellower
green) is from Caribbean slope of
Central America, from Veracruz,
Mexico, south to extreme western
Panama; *A. n. vicinalis* (brighter green
than *astec* with underparts greener, less
brownish) occurs in north-eastern
Mexico. Latter 2 sub-species are often
separated and given name of Astec or
Olive-throated Conure.
Status Common in woodland and
cultivated areas but declining in
Mexico, where most parrots are
threatened by habitat destruction.
Aviculture Always rare because
Jamaica has never legally exported
birds on a commercial basis; there
is no record of its being imported
into Europe before 1981 or of it
or *astec* being bred; a few *astec*
were imported into Europe during
1980s.
Accommodation 7 or 8.
Diet 7.
Clutch size 4 or 5.
Incubation Probably 25 days.
Young in nest Probably 8 weeks.

Petz, Orange-fronted or Half-moon Conure
Aratinga canicularis

German Elfenbeinsittich   **Dutch** Petzparkiet

Length 24 cm (9½ in).
Weight About 73 g (2½ oz).
Immatures Some have less orange on forehead; iris brown.
Origin Central America, Pacific slope from Sinaloa, northern Mexico, through Guatemala, El Salvador and Nicaragua to Costa Rica; range coincides with that of colonial termite, in whose termitaria it nests.
Status Common in lowlands and, in some regions, lower subtropical zone out of breeding season, in forest, scrubland and cultivated areas.
Aviculture Once very popular in USA as a pet and mimic, it is now rarely imported and rarely bred (termitaria-nesters are difficult to breed).
Accommodation 7.
Diet 7.
Clutch size 3–5.
Incubation 23 or 24 days.
Young in nest 7 weeks.

Brown-throated Conure or St Thomas Conure
Aratinga pertinax

German Braunwangensittich, St Thomassittich   **Dutch** St Thomasparkiet

Length 25 cm (10 in).
Weight 85–100 g (3–3½ oz).
Immatures Cheeks brown, throat and upper breast greenish (nominate race); 14 sub-species recognized; in those with less colour on head, immatures hardly vary from adults.
Origin Nominate race occurs on island of Curaçao, Netherlands Antilles; introduced to St Thomas, Virgin Islands; other sub-species occur in Panama and throughout much of northern South America north of the Amazon, and islands off coast of Venezuela.

Status Common, mainly in lowlands, in a variety of habitats, in some regions benefiting from forest clearance.
Aviculture Formerly common; now uncommon because within its range only Guyana exports birds; limited breeding.
Accommodation 7.
Diet 7.
Clutch size 3–5.
Incubation 23 or 24 days.
Young in nest 7 weeks.

The nominate race is illustrated but in recent years only *A. p. chrysophrys* from Guyana has been imported. It has a narrow orange line around eye; cheeks and ear coverts are brown, tinged orange, and crown and nape are green.

Cactus Conure *Aratinga cactorum*

German Kaktussittich **Dutch** Cactusparkiet

Length 25 cm (10 in).
Weight 75 g (2½ oz).
Immatures Plumage throughout paler; cere whiter.
Origin Eastern Brazil in the states of Bahia, Minas Gerais, Pernambuco, Ceará and Maranhão.
Status Locally common or very common in caatinga scrubland (low thorny scrub, low trees and cacti) and semi-desert areas.
Aviculture Rare (no legal export from Brazil); rarely bred.
Accommodation 7.
Diet 7.
Clutch size 4–6.
Incubation 25 days.
Young in nest 7 weeks; sexual maturity: a captive-bred female has laid at 13 months.

International cooperation between aviculturists will probably be needed if this species is not to die out in captivity; as it is not rare in the wild or valuable within aviculture, it seems unlikely to be established. However, possibly in Brazil it will be bred to several generations in the attempt to establish the yellow mutation owned by a prominent aviculturist.

Golden-crowned or Peach-fronted Conure *Aratinga aurea*

German Goldstirnsittich   **Dutch** Goudvoorhoofdparkiet

Length 26 cm (10 in).
Weight 80 g (3 oz).
Immatures Slightly duller head coloration; upper mandible or both mandibles pale pinkish-white.
Origin Surinam (southern tip) and a large area of Brazil, mainly south of the Amazon, southwards through Paraguay into north-western Argentina.
Status Common or locally common, even increasing in some localities; inhabits woodlands, scrubby vegetation, savannah and cultivated areas.
Aviculture One of the most popular and well-known members of the genus, but now less common; fairly limited breeding.
Accommodation 7.
Diet 7.
Clutch size Usually 4, but 2–6 recorded.
Incubation 24 days.
Young in nest 7–8 weeks.

This is one of the most attractive members of the genus, being pretty, not too noisy and very willing to nest. They are usually excellent parents. A pair in the author's care favoured fresh corn and bread and milk while rearing young.

Nanday Conure *Nandayus nenday*

German Nandaysittich	**Dutch** Nandayaparkiet

Length 31 cm (12 in).
Weight 140 g (5 oz).
Immatures Less blue on upper breast and shorter tail.
Origin Bolivia (south-eastern region), Brazil (southern Mato Grosso), Paraguay and Argentina (northern provinces of Formosa and Chaco); feral populations have become established in southern USA.

Status Common in open country.
Aviculture Common and inexpensive; imported in large numbers from Argentina and Bolivia; free-breeding.
Accommodation 7 or 8.
Diet 7.
Clutch size 3–5.
Incubation 24 days.
Young in nest 8 weeks.

Although handsome and relatively low-priced, it is not popular with many breeders because of its loud voice. However, hand-reared young are much less noisy and make superb pets, being affectionate and playful. They are ideal for someone who wants a pet they can handle but who cannot afford a high-priced species such as an Amazon.

Yellow-eared Conure   *Ognorhynchus icterotis*

German Gelbohrsittich   **Dutch** Geeloorparkiet

Length 42 cm (16½ in).
Weight 285 g (10 oz).
Immatures Undescribed, but probably with paler beak, lighter eye skin and brownish iris.
Origin Andes of northern Ecuador (Imbabura and Pichincha) and Colombia (Caldas).
Status Rare; endangered by deforestation; occurs between 2,000 m (6,600 ft) and 3,500 m (11,550 ft), often in association with wax palms (*Ceroxylon andiculum*); on Appendix 1 of CITES.
Aviculture An extreme rarity – literally only 2 or 3 birds have been known, 2 of which were imported into UK in about 1965, at different times. This species is macaw-like in some respects, including the fact that the naked skin beside the lower mandible 'blushes' when the bird is excited.

Clutch size, incubation period and length of time young remain in nest are unknown.

Lesser Patagonian Conure *Cyanoliseus patagonus patagonus*

German Kleiner Felsensittich, Patagoniensittich
Dutch Patagonische rotsparkiet

Length 45 cm (18 in).
Weight 240–310 g (8½–11 oz); newly hatched chicks weigh 10 g (⅓ oz).
Immatures Upper mandible white, gradually becoming black from the sides; iris grey.
Origin Central and southern Argentina; *C. p. andinus* (little or no yellow on underparts) is from north-western Argentina.
Status Locally common but declining due to persecution (considered an agricultural pest, it is poisoned and its nests are destroyed) and trapping for export.
Aviculture Common and free-breeding; beautiful but very noisy.
Accommodation 5; 1 or 2 pairs will breed in same aviary – more than this and only dominant pair will breed.
Diet 13.
Clutch size 3–5.
Incubation 24 or 25 days.
Young in nest 53–63 days.

Greater Patagonian Conure *Cyanoliseus patagonus byroni*

German Grosser Felsensittich   **Dutch** Grote patagonische rotsparkiet

Length 53 cm (21 in).
Weight 3 adults weighed 315 g (11 oz), 345 g (12 oz) and 390 g (14 oz); newly hatched chicks weigh 12 g (nearly $\frac{1}{2}$ oz).
Immatures Upper mandible white, gradually becoming black from sides; iris grey.
Origin Central Chile.
Status Formerly abundant, now rare; only 10 nesting colonies are known to survive and fewer than 3,000 individuals.
Aviculture Rare; breeding in only 3 or 4 collections.
Accommodation 6; a single pair per aviary most successful in author's experience.
Diet 13.
Clutch size 2–4.
Incubation About 25 days.
Young in nest 8–9 weeks.

Blue-throated Conure *Pyrrhura cruentata*

German Blaulatzsittich   **Dutch** Blauwkeelparkiet

Length 28 cm (11 in).
Weight 90 g (3 oz); newly hatched
chicks weigh 5 or 6 g (about $\frac{1}{5}$ oz).
Immatures Plumage slightly duller,
with less red on bend of wing; iris
greyish.
Origin Eastern Brazil from southern
Bahia to south-eastern Minas Gerais.
Status Destruction and fragmentation
of forest has caused a serious decline in
its numbers; it is on Appendix 1 of
CITES.
Aviculture Rare; limited but
increasing breeding.
Accommodation 7.
Diet 7a (favourite food – guavas!).
Clutch size 4–7.
Incubation 22 days.
Young in nest 7–8 weeks; sexually
mature at 2–3 years.

This is one of the least typical members of the genus in both appearance and
behaviour; females tend to be heavier than males and more dominant and assertive.
Ultimately its survival may depend on captive breeding.

Red-bellied Conure *Pyrrhura frontalis*

German Braunohrsittich   **Dutch** Bruinoorparkiet

Length 26 cm (10 in).
Weight 70 g (2½ oz); newly hatched chicks weigh 4 or 5 g (about ⅙ oz).
Immatures Slightly duller, usually with less red on abdomen.
Origin South-eastern Brazil, Uruguay, eastern Paraguay and northern Argentina.
Status Common in a wide variety of habitats, even those disturbed by humans.
Aviculture Always most common member of genus; free-breeding.
Accommodation 7.
Diet 7a.
Clutch size 4–6.
Incubation 22 days.
Young in nest 7–8 weeks.

Some pairs are prolific, especially in warm climates. One pair reared 14 in 3 nests. They can be aggressive towards other parrots, even larger species.

Recent chromosome analysis indicates that it and *P. molinae* are *not* separate species; there is evidence of gene flow between the 2 populations, which have adjacent ranges with an area of overlap (Valentine, 1987).

Crimson-bellied Conure
*Pyrrhura perlata perlata (*formerly *Pyrrhura rhodogaster)*

German Blausteiss-sittich (formerly Rotbauchsittich)
Dutch Roodbuikparkiet

Length 25 cm (10 in).
Weight 85 g (3 oz).
Immatures Underparts green, colours duller and greener throughout; beak pale greyish; the first red breast feathers appear at about 6 months. Two immatures are illustrated; the bird on the left is slightly older.
Origin Brazil, just south of the Amazon River (western Pará-Tapajós River), westwards to eastern Amazonas and southwards to central-western Mato Grosso.
Status Common in some areas but little is known generally.
Aviculture Rare but free-breeding and increasing, especially in Europe.
Accommodation 7.
Diet 7a.
Clutch size 4–6.
Incubation 24 days.
Young in nest About 7 weeks.

Pearly Conure *Pyrrhura perlata lepida*

German Blauwangensittich   **Dutch** Parelparkiet

Length 24 cm (9½ in).
Weight 70 g (2½ oz).
Immatures Like adults but usually with lighter-grey beak.
Origin Brazil, north-eastern region; *P. p. lepida* is from Pará (Belém and Capim River) east to Cuma Bay, Maranhão); *P. p. coerulescens* (paler brown on nape and crown, upper cheeks green, lower cheeks blue, more blue on upper breast) is known only from Miritiba, northern Maranhão; and *P. p. anerythra* (green under-wing coverts; red in other sub-species) is also from Pará (Fresco River, Pracupi River and Tocantins River).
Status Serious decline in recent years due to deforestation; generally uncommon.
Aviculture Uncommon to rare; fairly free-breeding so increase is likely.
Accommodation 7.
Diet 7a.
Clutch size 3–5, occasionally 6.
Incubation 24 or 25 days.
Young in nest 7–8 weeks.

The sub-species *lepida* is illustrated but identification can be difficult; note that *lepida* has blue cheeks, with green only towards the lores.

Green-cheeked Conure *Pyrrhura molinae*

German Grünwangen-Rotschwanzsittich   **Dutch** Molinaparkiet

Length 26 cm (10 in).
Weight 60–80 g (2–3 oz), depending on sub-species; newly hatched chicks weigh 5 g ($\frac{1}{6}$ oz).
Immatures Slightly duller with little or no red on abdomen.
Origin West-central Brazil, Mato Grosso; northern and eastern Bolivia; north-west Argentina; possibly also northern Paraguay.

Status Fairly common in a variety of habitats, at various altitudes.
Aviculture Almost unknown until late 1970s; fairly common and free-breeding.
Accommodation 7.
Diet 7a.
Clutch size 4–6.
Incubation 22–24 days.
Young in nest 7 weeks.

Five sub-species recognized; illustrated is *P. m. australis* from southern Bolivia and north-west Argentina. It has less blue in plumage than nominate race and larger red abdominal patch than *P. m. sordida*, both of which have been exported.

White-eared Conure *Pyrrhura leucotis*

German Weissohrsittich   **Dutch** Witoorparkiet

Length 23 cm (9 in).
Weight 50 g ($1\frac{3}{4}$ oz) (nominate race);
newly hatched chicks weigh 3 or 4 g
(about $\frac{1}{8}$ oz).
Immatures Brazilian sub-species:
softer coloration overall,
less-pronounced barred breast, duller
and smaller maroon patch on
abdomen; cere and eye skin whitish
(grey in adults).
Origin The sub-species *P. l. emma* and
P. l. auricularis, both with forecrown
blue, are from northern Venezuela.
There are 3 sub-species from eastern
Brazil: the nominate (illustrated)
from southern Bahia to São Paulo;
P. l. griseipectus (no blue suffusion on
forecrown, whiter ear coverts) is from

Ceará in north-eastern Brazil; and
P. l. pfrimeri (chestnut forehead) is
from Goiás.
Status Marked decline, rare and local
in south-eastern Brazil; locally
common in Venezuela.
Aviculture Rare to fairly rare;
free-breeding.
Accommodation 7.
Diet 7a.
Clutch size Usually 4 or 5, but
between 3 and 8.
Incubation 20 days optimum
conditions, but up to 24 days in a large
clutch.
Young in nest 42–48 days.
Sexually mature At about 15 months;
some pairs are double-brooded.

Painted Conure   *Pyrrhura picta*

German Blaustirn-Rotschwanzsittich   **Dutch** Picta

Length 23 cm (9 in).
Weight 55 g (2 oz).
Immatures Duller, bend of wing green with few scattered red feathers; eye skin whitish (grey in adults).
Origin The Amazon basin: Guianas, Venezuela, Brazil, Peru and northern Bolivia; also north-western Colombia and central Panama.
Status Common (except in Colombia), especially in lowland humid forest.
Aviculture Almost unknown until mid-1970s; remains uncommon yet free-breeding.
Accommodation 7.
Diet 7a.
Clutch size 4–8, usually 5–7.
Incubation 23 days.
Young in nest 40–51 days recorded.

Nine sub-species of widely differing appearance are recognized. The nominate race (illustrated) is the best known. The most striking is the Brazilian form *P. p. roseifrons*, which has forehead, lores and forecrown red. In aviculture, it is virtually unknown outside Brazil.

Demerara or Fiery-shouldered Conure *Pyrrhura egregria*

German Demerarasittich   **Dutch** Demeraraparkiet

Length 25 cm (10 in).
Weight About 75 g (2½ oz).
Immatures Less yellow and orange on bend of wing; carpal edge and under-wing coverts green, crown and nape green; iris greyish.
Origin Venezuela, south-eastern region and adjoining western Guyana and extreme north-eastern Roraima, Brazil.
Status Common in its limited range –

forest between 700 m (2,300 ft) and 1,800 m (6,000 ft).
Aviculture Apparently unknown until 1988, when a few were imported into Europe.
Accommodation 7.
Diet 7a.
Clutch size 4 or 5.
Incubation 23 days*.
Young in nest 7 weeks*.

Black-tailed Conure *Pyrrhura melanura*

German Schwarzschwanzsittich   **Dutch** Bruinstaartparkiet

Length 24 cm (10 in).
Weight 85 g (3 oz).
Immatures Fainter markings on breast; beak slightly paler.
Origin Central Colombia, southern Venezuela south to north-western Brazil, Ecuador and northern Peru.
Status Common but patchily distributed; occurs in forested and partly deforested areas at all altitudes.
Aviculture Rare until 1967 and following decade; remains uncommon to rare; limited breeding.
Accommodation 7.
Diet 7a.
Clutch size 4 or 5.
Incubation 23 days.
Young in nest 7 weeks.

Five sub-species are recognized, although *P. m. souancei* (illustrated) and *P. m. berlepschi* may prove synonymous. They differ from the nominate race in more extensive red on primary wing coverts, but no yellow; light margins to feathers of upper breast and neck are broader and more conspicuous.

Rock or Black-capped Conure *Pyrrhura rupicola*

German Steinsittich   **Dutch** Zwartkapparkiet

Length 25 cm (10 in).
Weight 70 g (2½ oz).
Immatures Duller throughout and
less red on carpal edge of wing; paler
beak and white cere.
Origin Peru, central and
south-eastern regions, northern
Bolivia, extreme north-western Brazil.
Status Generally uncommon but
locally common, mainly in humid

lowland forests.
Aviculture Probably unknown until
1980; remains uncommon; limited
breeding.
Accommodation 7.
Diet 7a.
Clutch size 5–7 or more; 10 laid by a
female in author's care.
Incubation 23 or 24 days.
Young in nest 7–8 weeks.

Austral Conure *Enicognathus ferrugineus*

German Smaragdsittich   **Dutch** Magelhaenparkiet, Smaragdparkiet

Length *E. f. ferrugineus* 35 cm (14 in), *E. f. minor* 31 cm (12½ in).
Weight *E. f. minor* 160 g (5½ oz).
Immatures Less maroon on abdomen; eye skin whitish (grey in adults).
Origin Southernmost Chile (Magallanes province) and southern Argentina (eastern slopes of Andes); *minor* is from southern Chile (Colchagua south to Aysén) and south-western Argentina.

Status Common in Nothofagus and other forests.
Aviculture Almost unknown until 1970; occasionally imported during 1980s; limited breeding although it nests readily.
Accommodation 8.
Diet 7a.
Clutch size 5 or 6.
Incubation 26 days.
Young in nest 53–63 days.

The sub-species *minor* is illustrated. Nominate race is very rare in aviculture; it is lighter green with lighter and larger red patch on abdomen.

Slender-billed Conure *Enicognathus leptorhynchus*

German Langschnabelsittich   **Dutch** Langsnavelparkiet

Length 41 cm (16 in).
Weight 240 g ($8\frac{1}{2}$ oz); newly hatched chicks weigh 10 g ($\frac{1}{3}$ oz).
Immatures Shorter tail; eye skin white; shorter beak.
Origin Central Chile (Aconcagua south to Chiloé Island).
Status Locally common in forest and farmland, but declining due to deforestation, hunting and Newcastle disease.
Aviculture Almost unknown until 1976, since when irregularly imported; fairly free-breeding – some pairs prolific.
Accommodation 7 or 8.
Diet 7a.
Clutch size 4–6.
Incubation 26 days.
Young in nest 7 weeks.

Thick-billed Parrot *Rhynchopsitta pachyrhynchus*

German Arasittich   **Dutch** Diksnavelparkiet

Length 38 cm (15 in).
Weight 300 g (10½ oz); a newly
hatched chick weighed 10 g (⅓ oz).
Immatures Red confined to forehead;
lack red above eye and on bend and
carpal edge of wing, which are green;
bill horn-coloured with dark grey at
base of upper mandible.
Origin Mexico, highlands of northern
and central regions (Sierra Madre
Occidental in Chihuahua and eastern
Sonora southwards to Michoacán); a
release programme for wild-caught
captive birds commenced in 1986 in
Chiricahua mountains of south-eastern
Arizona, USA; the species formerly
occurred in Arizona and New Mexico,
last reports being in 1935.
Status Rare and declining due to
destruction of pine forests, its only
habitat; on Appendix 1 of CITES.
Aviculture Rare; slightly more
common in USA as a result of birds
entering illegally; limited breeding.
Accommodation 5.
Diet 12.
Clutch size 2–4, occasionally 1.
Incubation 26–8 days reported.
Young in nest 8–9 weeks; it nests late
in year, about August.

Quaker or Monk Parrakeet   *Myiopsitta monachus*

German Mönchsittich   **Dutch** Muisparkiet, Monniksparkiet

Length 29 cm (11 in).
Weight 150 g (5½ oz).
Immatures Forehead tinged with green; shorter tail.
Origin South-eastern South America from central Bolivia and southern Brazil south to central Argentina; feral populations established in USA and elsewhere.
Status Except in central Bolivia this species is extremely abundant, often in large flocks mainly in lowlands.
Aviculture Always common; imported in large numbers; free-breeding.
Accommodation 8.
Diet 7a.
Clutch size 5–7.
Incubation 23 or 24 days.
Young in nest 6–7 weeks.

This species nests in colonies, building from twigs a large, bulky nest which has a number of nesting chambers. In an aviary pairs will build their own nest if provided with a welded mesh base and a large supply of twigs. Nest-boxes may be used.

Aymara or Sierra Parrakeet *Bolborhynchus aymara*

German Aymarasittich   **Dutch** Aymaraparkiet

Length 20 cm (8 in).
Weight 45 g (1½ oz).
Immatures Shorter tail.
Origin Cental Bolivia south to north-western Argentina.
Status Fairly common between 1,800 m (6,000 ft) and 3,000 m (10,000 ft) but up to 4,000 m (13,200 ft).
Aviculture Occasionally imported since 1961; however, mortality in newly imported birds is too high for trade to be acceptable; fairly free-breeding.

Accommodation 9.
Diet 5, including seeding grasses.
Clutch size 6–10, 12 known.
Incubation Not recorded exactly because incubation does not commence with first egg, thus its hatching has occurred 28–30 days after laying; also incubation tends to be lengthened in large clutches; probable period for last egg is 22 days.
Young in nest 6–7 weeks.
Sexual dimorphism Male is darker grey on crown and more silvery-grey on breast.

Mountain Parrakeet *Bolborhynchus aurifrons*

German Zitronensittich   **Dutch** Citroenparkiet

Length 18 cm (7 in).
Weight 45 g (1½ oz).
Immatures Like female; shorter tail.
Origin Central Peru (coast and western slopes of Andes); *B. a. robertsi* is from north-western Peru (Marañon Valley); *B. a. margaritae* from southern Peru and central-western Bolivia through northern Chile to north-western Argentina; *B. a. rubrirostris* occurs in north-western Argentina.
Status Locally common up to 4,000 m (13,200 ft) on steppes, open shrubby areas, cultivated land and even city parks.
Aviculture Rare until late 1960s, since when occasionally imported; mortality rate is very high; calcium and Vitamin D₃ supplementation is essential for high-altitude species.
Accommodation 9.
Diet 5, with unlimited additional fruits.
Clutch size About 5*.
Incubation 23 days*.
Young in nest 7 weeks*.
Sexual dimorphism In nominate race only male has face and underparts yellow. In *margaritae* (illustrated) both sexes are like female of nominate race; male's beak is light-horn colour, female's is grey. In *robertsi* male is dark green below with yellow throat and yellowish beak; female's beak is darker. Plumage is bluer green above in *rubrirostris* and grey-green below; beak reddish-horn in adult male and grey in female.

Lineolated or Barred Parrakeet *Bolborhynchus lineola*

German Katharinasittich   **Dutch** Catharinaparkiet

Length 16 cm (6½ in).
Weight 50 g (1½ oz).
Immatures Less heavy barring; bluer tinge on forehead.
Origin Mexico to Panama: probably continuous distribution through Guatemala, Honduras, Costa Rica, etc., except in central and eastern Panama (mountains not high), thence from westernmost Venezuela through Colombia, Ecuador and central Peru.
Status Difficult to determine (migratory) but probably locally common or scarce, in some areas preferring dense high-altitude forest or cloud forest.
Aviculture Occasionally imported; some are free-breeding; well established in parts of Europe (e.g. Netherlands), where mutations are bred.
Accommodation 9.
Diet 5, plus egg-rearing food; nectar relished.
Clutch size 3–6, usually 4 or 5.
Incubation 18 days.
Young in nest 5 weeks.

Can be bred on colony system; must never be housed with larger birds.

Spectacled Parrotlet *Forpus conspicillatus*

German Augenring-Sperlingspapagei   **Dutch** Gebrilde dwergpapegaai

Length 11 cm ($4\frac{1}{2}$ in).
Weight 30 g (1 oz).
Immatures Males: emerald green around eye; blue on rump and wings mixed with green; females: like adult.
Origin Panama (eastern region), Colombia (except south-east) and western Venezuela.
Status Common to uncommon and local.
Aviculture Common in some European countries (e.g. Denmark, Germany), rare elsewhere; free-breeding.
Accommodation 9.
Diet 5.
Clutch size 4–6.
Incubation 18 days.
Young in nest About 5 weeks; can be sexed on leaving nest.
Sexual dimorphism A male is illustrated. The female is a much yellower shade of green and entirely lacks blue in plumage; her lower back, rump and cheeks are bright green.

It is not advisable to ring chicks in the nest as the parents usually try to remove the rings, resulting in mutilated chicks.

Celestial or Pacific Parrotlet *Forpus coelestis*

German Blaugenick-Sperlingspapagei   **Dutch** Grijsrug-dwergpapegaai

Length 13 cm (5 in).
Weight 33 g (1 oz).
Immatures Duller; blue in males is less extensive and paler and, on rump, mixed with bluish-green.
Origin Ecuador, western region, south to north-western Peru.
Status Fairly common in dry open or semi-open country.
Aviculture Almost unknown until 1960s, but now well established through captive breeding.
Accommodation 3 (aggression between male and female often occurs in a small cage).
Diet 5.
Clutch size 4–6.
Incubation 18 days.
Young in nest 4–5 weeks; can be sexed at 4 weeks.
Sexual dimorphism Female lacks cobalt markings on rump.

Despite their small size, they can be aggressive and should not be kept with other small parrots.

Yellow-faced Parrotlet *Forpus xanthops*

German Gelbmasken-Sperlingspapagai   **Dutch** Geelkop-dwergpapegaai

Length 14.5 cm (6 in).
Weight 35 g (1 oz).
Immatures Slightly duller, with reduced area of yellow on head; no dark mark on beak.
Origin Peru: upper Marañón Valley in north-west.
Status Locally common in very restricted range; vulnerable to habitat destruction by goats (inhabits desert scrubland, also river edges).
Aviculture Unknown until 1979; still rare, although some pairs are prolific.

It is important to establish this species.
Accommodation 3.
Diet 5.
Clutch size 3–6, usually 5 or 6.
Incubation 22 days*.
Young in nest 5–6 weeks; usually double-brooded.
Sexual dimorphism: A male is illustrated; female has lower back and rump pale blue and primary and secondary coverts green tinged with blue.

All-green or Plain Parrakeet *Brotogeris tirica*

German Tirikasittich   **Dutch** Tiricaparkiet

Length 23 cm (9 in).
Weight 63 g (2½ oz); a newly hatched chick weighed 3 g (1/10 oz).
Immatures Tail much shorter; base of upper mandible dark brown.
Origin Eastern Brazil, from Alagoas and eastern Bahia south to São Paulo or Santa Catarina.
Status Fairly common to common in lowlands in various habitats, even city parks and gardens.
Aviculture Rare (like all species endemic to south-east Brazil); rarely bred.
Accommodation 7.
Diet 7b.
Clutch size 4–6.
Incubation 24 days.
Young in nest About 38 days.

Few captive breedings of any *Brotogeris* are recorded; they apparently need the stimulus of the sight or sound of other members of genus. Colony breeding could be attempted in a large aviary.

Canary-winged Parrakeet *Brotogeris versicolurus chiriri*

German Kanarienflügelsittich   **Dutch** Kanarievleugelparkiet

Length 22 cm (9 in).
Weight 70 g (2½ oz).
Immatures Darker beak, quickly changing to adult colour.
Origin Brazil: eastern and southern regions; northern and eastern Bolivia, Paraguay and northern Argentina.
Status Common in open woodland, mainly in lowland areas.

Aviculture Less common than formerly; large numbers have been exported but breeding successes are rare.
Accommodation 7.
Diet 7b.
Clutch size 3–6.
Incubation 26 days*.
Young in nest 7 weeks*.

Further research may show that *B. v. chiriri* is specifically distinct from the White-winged Parrakeet (*B. v. versicolurus*), with which it is easily confused. The latter is a bluer shade of green, with some of the primaries and all the secondaries white.

Orange-flanked or Grey-cheeked Parrakeet
Brotogeris pyrrhopterus

German Feuerflügelsittich   **Dutch** Vuurvleugelparkiet

Length 20 cm (8 in).
Weight 45–60 g (about 2 oz).
Immatures Beak dark brown and feet grey (pink in adults).
Origin Ecuador, western region, west of Andes, to extreme north-western Peru.
Status Rare and local in Ecuador (decline due to habitat destruction and trapping); fairly common in Peru in lowland deciduous forest.
Aviculture Common until early 1970s; now much rarer and seldom bred.
Accommodation 7.
Diet 7b.
Clutch size 4 or 5.
Incubation 25–26 days.
Young in nest 6 weeks (author's experience, but others quote up to 8).

Imported young birds used to be extremely popular pets; hand-reared captive-bred birds are even more attractive and playful. However, it is important to retain young for breeding if this species is to survive in aviculture.

Tovi or Orange-chinned Parrakeet *Brotogeris jugularis*

German Tovisittich, Goldkinnsittich   **Dutch** Toviparkiet

Length 18 cm (7 in).
Weight 58 g (2 oz).
Immatures Described as resembling adults but one would expect the beak to be darker on fledging.
Origin Mexico (south-west); Central America, south to northern Colombia and northern Venezuela.
Status Common in most types of woodland, even disturbed forest, but especially lightly wooded areas.
Aviculture Once common, now much rarer as there are no major exporting countries within its range; rarely bred.
Accommodation 7.
Diet 7b.
Clutch size 4–8.
Incubation 25–27 days*.
Young in nest 5–6 weeks*.

Cobalt-winged Parrakeet   *Brotogeris cyanoptera*

German Blauflügelsittich   **Dutch** Kobaltvleugelparkiet

Length 18 cm (7 in).
Weight 65 g (2½ oz).
Immatures Orange chin spot duller, forehead and lores only tinged with yellow; upper mandible dark brown, feet grey.
Origin Western part of Amazon basin: southern Venezuela, south-eastern Colombia and north-western Brazil south to

northern Bolivia.
Status Common in lowland forest.
Aviculture Occasionally available; seldom bred.
Accommodation 7.
Diet 7b.
Clutch size 3–6.
Incubation About 24 days*.
Young in nest 7 weeks.

Golden-winged Parrakeet *Brotogeris chrysopterus*

German Goldflügelsittich   **Dutch** Oranjevleugelparkiet

Length 16 cm (6 in).
Weight 65 g (2½ oz).
Immatures Primary coverts green (orange in adults); beak colour undescribed but one would expect it to be darker.
Origin Guianas, eastern Venezuela and northern Brazil.
Status Fairly common in lowland forests.
Aviculture Always uncommon; no captive breeding known to author.

Accommodation 7.
Diet 7b; natural diet consists of fruits, flowers, water snails and algae; its beak shape may be adapted to removing water snails from their shells, something which it is believed no other parrot can do.
Clutch size 3 or 4.
Incubation Not recorded, probably 24 days*.
Young in nest Not recorded, probably 7 weeks.

Tui Parrakeet *Brotogeris sanctithomae*

German Tuisittich   **Dutch** Tuiparkiet

Length 17 cm (7 in).
Weight 58 g (2 oz).
Immatures Iris dark grey; beak darker brown.
Origin Nominate race is from Brazil, mouth of Madeira River, eastern Amazonas, west to north-eastern Peru and extreme south-eastern Colombia, and along Madeira River to northern Bolivia and south-eastern Peru; the sub-species *B. s. takatsukasae* is from northern Brazil (mouth of Maderia River, eastern Amazonas, east to Amapá and south to the mouth of the Curuá River).
Status Common in seasonally flooded forest and clearings; also inhabits open country.
Aviculture Formerly common; rare since Brazil ceased to export birds, and rarely bred.
Accommodation 7.
Diet 7b.
Clutch size 4 or 5.
Incubation Not recorded but probably 24 days.
Young in nest 45 days* (single reference only).

The sub-species *B. s. takatsukasae* is illustrated. The nominate race lacks the yellow behind the eye.

Black-headed Caique *Pionites melanocephala*

German Grünzügelpapagei   **Dutch** Zwartcopcaique

Length 23 cm (9 in).
Weight 160 g (5½ oz); newly hatched chicks weigh 8 g (⅓ oz).
Immatures Underparts yellowish-white or pale buff; wings tinged with blue; beak horn-coloured marked with black; iris dark brown.
Origin North of the Amazon in the Guianas, northern Brazil, north-eastern and southern Venezuela and south-eastern Colombia.
Status Fairly common in lowland forest (canopy and margins).
Aviculture Regularly imported from Guyana in small numbers; breeding limited but increasing.
Accommodation 7 (preferably secluded not open surroundings).
Diet 13, with emphasis on fruit.
Clutch size 3.
Incubation 25–27 days (27 in author's experience).
Young in nest 10 weeks.

The fearless, inquisitive and playful personality of caiques, especially when hand-reared, make them among the most delightful of pet birds. The nominate race has orange thighs; sub-species *P. m. pallida* has thighs yellower.

White-bellied Caique *Pionites leucogaster*

German Rostkappenpapagei **Dutch** Witbuikcaique

Length 23 cm (9 in).
Weight 165 g (6 oz); newly hatched chicks weigh 7 g ($\frac{1}{4}$ oz).
Immatures Underparts yellowish-white; crown and area around eye heavily marked with black (a few black feathers being retained for up to 1 year); beak pinkish marked with black or mainly black; iris brown.
Origin Brazil, south of the Amazon, west to eastern Peru and possibly eastern Ecuador.

Status Common in lowland forests near rivers; less common in dry forests.
Aviculture Uncommon; limited breeding.
Accommodation 7 (preferably secluded surroundings).
Diet 13, with emphasis on fruit.
Clutch size 3, occasionally 4.
Incubation 24–27 days (27 in author's experience).
Young in nest 10 weeks.

The nominate race is illustrated; the sub-species *P. l. xanthomeria* has yellow thighs.

Red-capped or Pileated Parrot *Pionopsitta pileata*

German Scharlachkopfpapagei   **Dutch** Roodkapparkiet

Length 22 cm (9 in).
Weight 110 g (4 oz).
Immatures Males: usually only narrow band of red on forehead, bordered by orange-yellow band in some birds; two imported males at first lacked all red on head except for a tinge on ear coverts; females: like adult.
Origin Brazil, south-east from southern Bahia south to Rio Grande do Sul; eastern Paraguay and north-eastern Argentina (Misiones and Corrientes).
Status Overall decline due to deforestation but locally common where extensive forest remains; on Appendix 1 of CITES.
Aviculture Imported regularly between 1969 and 1976 only; now rare and seldom bred.
Accommodation 7 (secluded location).
Diet 7a, plus boiled maize.
Clutch size 3 or 4.
Incubation 24 or 25 days*.
Young in nest 47–54 days.
Sexual dimorphism As illustrated, the female lacks red on head.

This is a very sociable species which is most likely to breed within sight or sound of other *pileata*.

Vulturine Parrot　*Gypopsitta (or Pionopsitta) vulturina*

German Kahlkopfpapagei　　**Dutch** Gierpapegaai

Length 23 cm (9 in).
Weight Estimated 115 g (4 oz).
Immatures Head feathers green with yellow bases; bare skin surrounding eyes and lores brownish-yellow; yellow head feathers lacking; paler green below with less blue suffusion; bill yellowish, iris probably brownish.
Origin Brazil, north-east, south of the Amazon, eastern Amazonas south to southern Pará.
Status Either uncommon or overlooked; very little is known of this species.
Aviculture Probably never kept outside Brazil. A very experienced and dedicated Brazilian aviculturist has succeeded in keeping them alive for a few months only, finally giving up the attempt and releasing the survivors.
Diet In the wild it eats fruits, berries and seeds.
Young in nest No nesting data has been recorded.

A sub-adult (left) and an adult bird (right) are illustrated.

Originally placed in a monotypic genus because of the absence of most head feathers, it is sometimes more logically classified as *Pionopsitta*.

Short-tailed Parrot *Graydidascalus brachyurus*

German Kurzschwanzpapagei   **Dutch** Kortstaartpapegaai

Length 24 cm (9 in).
Weight 200 g (7 oz).
Immatures Said to lack red in tail; iris colour not recorded but probably brownish.
Origin Amazon basin: south–eastern Colombia, south to eastern Ecuador and eastern Peru and east to mouth of Amazon.
Status Common along rivers and in seasonally flooded areas.
Aviculture Rare; no successful breeding yet recorded.
Accommodation 7 (secluded location).
Diet 7a.
Clutch size 3–4*.
Incubation 24 or 25 days.
Young in nest Unknown.

Data relating to the last 3 entries here are from the late Mrs J. Spenkelink of the Netherlands.

Blue-headed Pionus *Pionus menstruus*

German Schwarzohrpapagei   **Dutch** Zwartoorpionus, Blauwkoppionus

Length 28 cm (11 in).
Weight 250 g (9 oz).
Immatures Much duller, head mainly dull green, some with red frontal band.
Origin Costa Rica, Panama and almost all of northern South America except the Andes.
Status Common in a wide range of habitats over an immense area; one of the most numerous of neotropical parrots.
Aviculture Always common but only recently bred with frequency.
Accommodation 7 or 8.
Diet 7 (chicken optional).
Clutch size 3 or 4.
Incubation 26 days.
Young in nest About 10 weeks.

Birds of this species, especially when hand-reared, make excellent pets, being quieter, smaller and more gentle than, for example, many Amazons.

Coral-billed or Sordid Pionus *Pionus sordidus*

German Dunenkopf   **Dutch** Koraalsnavelpionus

Length 28 cm (11 in).
Weight 255 g (9 oz).
Immatures Red band on forehead in some birds, less blue on head; under-tail coverts yellowish-green marked with red; upper mandible partly grey.
Origin Lower Andean slopes from northern Venezuela and western Colombia to Ecuador, eastern Peru and northern Bolivia.

Status Fairly common in forest and forest edges, up to about 1,500 m (5,000 ft).
Aviculture Uncommon; limited breeding but not difficult to breed.
Accommodation 7 or 8.
Diet 7 (chicken optional).
Clutch size 3.
Incubation 26 days.
Young in nest 9–10 weeks.

Illustrated is sub-species *P. s. corallinus* (from Colombia, Ecuador, Peru and Bolivia).

Maximilian's or Scaly-headed Pionus *Pionus maximiliani*

German Maximilian's Papagei   **Dutch** Maximiliaanpionus

Length 29 cm (11½ in).
Weight 230 g (8 oz); newly hatched chicks weigh 9 g (⅓ oz).
Immatures Less blue on upper breast; some birds have red frontal band.
Origin Brazil, from north-east southwards, through Bolivia and Paraguay to northern Argentina.
Status Fairly common in lowland forest (in Brazil up to 1,500 m, 5,000 ft).
Aviculture Fairly common; nests readily.
Accommodation 7 or 8.
Diet 7 (chicken optional).
Clutch size 4 or 5.
Incubation 26 days.
Young in nest 9–10 weeks.

The nominate race is illustrated. Sub-species vary mainly in colour of upper breast, which is darker blue in *P. m. melanoblepharus*, reddish-purple in *P. m. siy* and bluer reddish-purple and more extensive in *P. m. lacerus*.

Plum-crowned Pionus *Pionus tumultuosus tumultuosus*

German Rosenkopfpapagei   **Dutch** Pruimekoppionus

Length 29 cm (11½ in).
Weight 250 g (9 oz).
Immatures Nape, hindcrown, cheeks and breast green; under-tail coverts yellowish-green marked with pink at base.
Origin Peru, mountains of central and southern regions.
Status Generally uncommon but locally plentiful, usually at about 2,000 m (6,600 ft) to 2,800 m

(9,250 ft).
Aviculture Rare and rarely bred; in the USA, for example, there was not a single breeding pair at the time of writing.
Accommodation 7 or 8.
Diet 7 (chicken optional).
Clutch size 4.
Incubation 27 days.
Young in nest 9–10 weeks.

Formerly considered specifically distinct from Massena's Pionus (page 242). Little has been recorded about either.

Massena's or White-headed Pionus   *Pionus tumultuosus seniloides*

German Greisenkopfpapagei   **Dutch** Grijskoppionus

Length 28 cm (11 in).
Weight 250 g (9 oz); a newly hatched chick weighed 11 g (about $\frac{1}{3}$ oz).
Immatures Head feathers dull green with white bases to give speckled appearance; crown feathers margined with red in some birds; feathers of sides of head white, margined with dull green; breast green; eye skin white.
Origin Western Venezuela, western Colombia, western Ecuador and north-western Peru, in the Andes.
Status Believed scarcer than nominate race, but nomadic, little known and difficult to assess; inhabits forest between 2,000 m (6,600 ft) and 3,000 m (10,000 ft).
Aviculture Always rare; known to have bred in only 2 collections.
Accommodation 7 or 8.
Diet 7 (chicken optional).
Clutch size 4.
Incubation 28 days* (in author's experience of 2 eggs only).
Young in nest Unknown, assume 9–10 weeks.

White-crowned or White-capped Pionus *Pionus senilis*

German Weisskopfpapagei   **Dutch** Witkappionus

Length 24 cm ($9\frac{1}{2}$ in).
Weight 180 g ($6\frac{1}{2}$ oz).
Immatures Narrow band on forehead white; feathers of forecrown green and whitish; head otherwise green faintly tinged blue; chin, throat and breast green; under-tail coverts yellowish-green; skin surrounding eye white.
Origin Mexico, south-east region, through Central America to western Panama (mainly Caribbean slope).
Status Common and adaptable, being found on outskirts of towns and in partially cleared areas; may be extinct in western Nicaragua due to deforestation.
Aviculture Common in USA, less so elsewhere; second most frequently bred *Pionus* (after the Blue-headed, *P. menstruus*, page 238) in USA.
Accommodation 7.
Diet 7, without the chicken.
Clutch size 4–6.
Incubation 26 days.
Young in nest 8 weeks.

Bronze-winged Pionus *Pionus chalcopterus*

German Glanzflügelpapagei   **Dutch** Bronsvleugelpionus

Length 28 cm (11 in).
Weight 210 g (7½ oz).
Immatures Wings bronze, or wing feathers edged with green; feathers of underparts brown edged with dark green; skin surrounding eye yellowish.
Origin Venezuela (north-west), western Colombia, Ecuador and north-western Peru.
Status Locally plentiful in western Ecuador; elsewhere status difficult to determine – uncommon and nomadic; inhabits forest, mainly between 500 m (1,650 ft) and 2,000 m (6,600 ft).
Aviculture Uncommon; breeding infrequent except in 2 specialist *Pionus* collections (1 in UK, 1 in California).
Accommodation 7 or 8.
Diet 7 (chicken optional).
Clutch size 3 or 4.
Incubation 27 days.
Young in nest 9 weeks.

Overpreening of head feathers by a bird's mate sometimes occurs in this rather nervous, but very beautiful species.

Dusky Pionus *Pionus fuscus*

German Veilchenpapagei   **Dutch** Viooltjespapegaai

Length 24 cm (9½ in).
Weight 200 g (7 oz); newly hatched chicks weigh 9 g (⅓ oz).
Immatures Paler head with less distinct markings; bill pale yellow (on fledging); whitish cere and bare skin surrounding eye white (grey in adults).
Origin Venezuela, south-eastern region; Guianas to north-eastern Brazil; isolated population in northernmost Colombia.

Status Fairly common and widespread, mainly in lowland forests.
Aviculture Rare until the 1970s, since when small but regular exports from Guyana have occurred; limited breeding but not difficult to breed.
Accommodation 7 or 8.
Diet 7 (chicken optional).
Clutch size 4.
Incubation 26 days.
Young in nest 9–10 weeks.

Yellow-billed Amazon   *Amazona collaria*

German Jamaika–Amazone   **Dutch** Roodkeelamazone

Length 28 cm (11 in).
Weight 260 g (9 oz).
Immatures Plumage similar; upper mandible with dark markings.
Origin Jamaica.
Status Fairly common in forest and semi-forested areas but very vulnerable to deforestation.
Aviculture Always rare as no legal export of Jamaican birds; breeding limited but increasing.
Accommodation 8.
Diet 7.
Clutch size 3.
Incubation 26 days; 28 recorded for first egg.
Young in nest 8 weeks.

Cuban Amazon *Amazona leucocephala leucocephala*

German Kuba-Amazone   **Dutch** Cuba-amazone

Length 32 cm (13 in).
Weight 240 g ($8\frac{1}{2}$ oz); newly hatched chicks weigh 10 g ($\frac{1}{3}$ oz).
Immatures Less red on abdomen.
Origin Cuba, eastern and central regions.
Status Fairly common and increasing after years of habitat disturbance, shooting and trapping; on Appendix 1 of CITES.

Aviculture Rare until 1970s; greatly increased breeding but remains expensive; not difficult to breed, unlike sub-species *A. l. caymanensis*.
Accommodation 8.
Diet 7.
Clutch size 3–5, usually 4.
Incubation 27 or 28 days, but 25 has been recorded for last (third) egg.
Young in nest 8 weeks.

The sub-species *A. l. caymanensis* from Grand Cayman is rare in aviculture. It has a heavier build; forehead often suffused with pink or has yellow tinge; pink on head usually less extensive; turquoise wash on underparts.

Hispaniolan Amazon *Amazona ventralis*

German Blaukronenamazone   **Dutch** Hispaniolan-amazone

Length 28 cm (11 in).
Weight 240 g (8½ oz); newly hatched chicks weigh 10 g (⅓ oz).
Immatures White on forehead may be tinged with yellow; little or no red on abdomen; grey marks on upper mandible in very young birds.
Origin Hispaniola (divided politically into Haiti and Dominican Republic – not Dominica).
Status Locally abundant in Dominican Republic but threatened by deforestation; rarer in Haiti, where more deforestation has occurred.
Aviculture Uncommon; limited breeding; its aggressive nature makes it more difficult to breed than most small Amazons.
Accommodation 8.
Diet 7.
Clutch size 3 or 4.
Incubation 27–29 days.
Young in nest 9 weeks.

Spectacled Amazon *Amazona albifrons*

German Weiss-stirnamazone   **Dutch** Witfoorhoofdamazone

Length 26 cm (10 in).
Weight 235 g (8½ oz); *A. a. nana* about 205 g (7 oz).
Immatures Alula (coverts next to carpal edge of wing) green (red in adult males); both sexes less red and white on head and white tinged with yellow.
Origin Mexico (north-west) south through Guatemala, El Salvador and Nicaragua to Costa Rica.
Status Common in semi-open habitats, scrubby and gallery woodlands up to about 1,800 m

(6,000 ft).
Aviculture Fairly common; breeding limited but increasing.
Accommodation 8.
Diet 7.
Clutch size 3 or 4.
Incubation 24 and 25 days in incubator (Clarke, 1982); 26 days under female.
Young in nest 7–8 weeks.
Sexual dimorphism Male is illustrated; female usually has alula and primary coverts green.

Yellow-lored Amazon   *Amazona xantholora*

German Goldzügelamazone   **Dutch** Geelteugelamazone

Length 23 cm (9 in).
Weight 200 g (7 oz).
Immatures Sexable in the nest: males have red primary coverts; both sexes have forecrown blue and some yellow on lores; males may have a few red feathers near the eye or start to acquire these at about 5 months.
Origin Mexico in Yucatán Peninsula and Cozumel Island; also Belize.
Status Locally common, mainly in fairly open, dry country, including scrub and pine woodlands.
Aviculture Rare; rarely bred.
Accommodation 8.
Diet 7.
Clutch size 4 or 5.
Incubation About 26 days*.
Young in nest 7 or 8 weeks*.
Sexual dimorphism A female is illustrated; male has bright-yellow lores, forehead and forecrown white and red feathers encircling eye; also red primary coverts.

Tucuman Amazon *Amazona tucumana*

German Tucumanamazone   **Dutch** Tucumanamazone

Length 31 cm (12 in).
Weight 320 g (11½ oz).
Immatures Duller red forehead, followed by orange in some birds.
Origin South-eastern Bolivia and north-western Argentina.
Status Declining due to habitat destruction and, during 1980s, overtrapping; on Appendix 1 of CITES.
Aviculture Almost unknown until 1978, since when, until 1989, regularly

exported; limited but increasing breeding.
Accommodation 8.
Diet 7.
Clutch size 3.
Incubation 27 days*.
Young in nest 8 or 9 weeks*.
Sexual dimorphism Males have about 8 red coverts in each wing; females have from none to 6, but usually about 5.

Pretre's or Red-spectacled Amazon *Amazona pretrei*

German Prachtamazone   **Dutch** Prachtamazone, Roodbrilamazone

Length 31 cm (12 in).
Weight 260 g (9½ oz); newly hatched chicks 10 or 11 g (about ⅓ oz).
Immatures Red on crown less extensive, little or no red below eye or on carpal edge of wing; alula green (red in adults), much less red on primary coverts; thighs green (partly red in adults); iris pale grey; beak ivory.
Origin South-eastern Brazil (Rio Grande do Sul) and north-eastern Argentina (Misiones).
Status Serious decline in recent years due to clearance of *Araucaria* forest, its breeding habitat.

Aviculture Almost unknown until 1980s, when a few reached Europe; bred in 2 large collections in 1990 where the species should become firmly established.
Accommodation 8.
Diet 7.
Clutch size 3 or 4, occasionally 2.
Incubation 26 or 27 days*.
Young in nest 7–8 weeks.
Sexual dimorphism Red on forehead usually more extensive in males and always more extensive on carpal edge of wing and under-wing coverts. Males of less than perhaps 2 years might be confused with females in rare cases.

Green-cheeked Amazon *Amazona viridigenalis*

German Grünwangenamazone   **Dutch** Groenwangamazone

Length 33 cm (13 in).
Weight 270 g (9½ oz).
Immatures Crown green (only forehead and lores red); mauve markings duller and less extensive.
Origin North-eastern Mexico; feral population near Los Angeles, USA.
Status Decline in numbers and range due to habitat destruction and, until 1982, overtrapping for export.

Aviculture Common in USA, less so elsewhere; breeding increasing.
Accommodation 8.
Diet 7.
Clutch size 2–4.
Incubation 28 days.
Young in nest 9 weeks.
Sexual dimorphism Red on head usually less extensive in females.

Aviculturists must make a concerted effort to breed this species, especially in the USA, where it is still readily available.

Finsch's or Lilac-crowned Amazon   *Amazona finschi*

German Blaukappenamazone   **Dutch** Finschamazone

Length 33 cm (13 in).
Weight 325 g (11½ oz); newly hatched chicks weigh 11 g (about ⅓ oz).
Immatures Very slightly duller coloration; iris brownish and cere and skin surrounding eye white.
Origin Mexico, western region.
Status Common and widespread, mainly in wooded hills and mountains up to about 2,200 m (7,300 ft).
Aviculture Common in USA, fairly common in Europe; fairly frequently bred.
Accommodation 8.
Diet 7.
Clutch size 3.
Incubation 26 days.
Young in nest 54–60 days.

Primrose-cheeked or Red-lored Amazon
Amazona autumnalis autumnalis

German Gelbwangenamazone (*A. a. autumnalis*),
Ekuador-Amazone (*A. a. lilacina*)
Dutch Geelwangamazone

Length 34 cm (13½ in).
Weight About 350 g (12½ oz).
Immatures Less red on head, black margins to crown and nape poorly defined; iris is brown. In *A. a. lilacina* beak is whitish and grey; cere is light grey.
Origin Nominate race (illustrated above left) is found in Mexico (eastern – Caribbean – slope from Tamaulipas) south through Belize and Honduras to northern Nicaragua; *A. a. lilacina* is from western Ecuador, north of Gulf of Guayaquil.
Status Common in Central America; has probably declined in north-eastern

Mexico due to habitat destruction and trapping; however, it can exist in partially cleared areas; occurs up to about 800 m (2,650 ft). *A. a. lilacina* (illustrated above right) is declining due to habitat destruction.
Aviculture Nominate race is common in USA, slightly less so in Europe; fairly often bred. *A. a. lilacina* is considerably rarer, occasionally bred.
Accommodation 8.
Diet 7.
Clutch size 3.
Incubation 26 days*.
Young in nest 8–9 weeks.

Salvin's Amazon *Amazona autumnalis salvini*

German Salvin's Amazone (*A. a. salvini*), Diademamazone (*A. a. diadema*)
Dutch Salvinamazone

Length 35 cm (14 in).
Weight Females only 400 g (14 oz); males up to 550 g (19½ oz); *A. a. diadema*, 1 only (female), 480 g (17 oz).
Immatures Duller head coloration; iris brown.
Origin Nicaragua (south–east) and Costa Rica through Panama to western Colombia and north-western Venezuela. *A. a. diadema* is from north-western Brazil (lower Negro River region).
Status *A. a. salvini* is common in forested or wooded habitats throughout much of range; *A. a.*

diadema, status unknown.
Aviculture *A. a. salvini* uncommon and occasionally bred; *A. a. diadema* is rare, with breeding recorded in only 1 collection to date.
Accommodation 8.
Diet 7.
Clutch size 3; *diadema* 1 record only, 2.
Incubation 26 days*.
Young in nest 9 weeks.
Sexual dimorphism In *A. a. salvini* males have more extensive pink on throat and more pronounced mauve edges to nape feathers; female illustrated above left.

Both are noisy, excitable Amazons with attractive personalities. Note the key differences between the sub-species; *A. a. diadema* (illustrated above right) has cere partly or entirely feathered, and has green patch on crown.

Red-tailed Amazon *Amazona brasiliensis*

German Rotschwanzamazone   **Dutch** Roodstaartamazone

Length 35 cm (14 in).
Weight 430 g (15 oz).
Immatures Duller head coloration.
Origin Brazil, the coastal south-east region near São Paulo and Paraná.
Status Rare and declining; its range has contracted greatly due to deforestation; it once occurred throughout the coastal forests of south-eastern Brazil; on Appendix 1 of

CITES since 1981.
Aviculture Almost unknown until the 1980s, when a few birds reached Europe; no European breeding recorded by 1990.
Accommodation 8.
Diet 7.
Clutch size 2 or 3.
Incubation 28 days*.
Young in nest Assume 8 weeks.

Red-crowned Amazon *Amazona rhodocorytha*

German Granada-Amazone   **Dutch** Granada-Amazone

Length 36 cm (14 in).
Weight 450 g (16 oz).
Immatures Head markings less well defined; less extensive red markings on secondaries and on outer tail feathers; iris brown; eye skin white.
Origin Brazil, eastern coastal region: probably already extinct in the state of Rio de Janeiro and found only to the north in Espírito Santo and Bahia.
Status Declining, rare and locally distributed due to deforestation; on Appendix 1 of CITES.
Aviculture Extremely rare until 1980s, when a few reached Europe and USA; remains rare; limited breeding.
Accommodation 5 or 8.
Diet 7 (note that it is prone to obesity, so limit intake of fattening seeds and put emphasis on fruits and vegetables).
Clutch size 4.
Incubation 24 days*.
Young in nest Assume 8 weeks.
Sexual dimorphism Females usually have more extensive yellow extending downwards from lores.

Blue-cheeked Amazon *Amazona dufresniana*

German Goldmaskenamazone   **Dutch** Goudmaskeramazone

Length 36 cm (14 in).
Weight 490 g (17½ oz).
Immatures Undescribed, probably like adults with iris brown.
Origin Guianas and southern Venezuela.
Status Believed uncommon, but little information.
Aviculture Rare; a few birds exported from Guyana during 1980s but mortality in newly imported birds regrettably high; no captive breeding yet reported.
Accommodation 5 or 8.
Diet As for Red-crowned Amazon (opposite). Breeding information unknown but probably as for Red-crowned Amazon.

This species has a placid temperament and appears less active than many Amazons.

Festive Amazon   *Amazona festiva festiva*

German Blaubartamazone   **Dutch** Blaubaardamazone

Length 34 cm (13 in).
Weight 370 g (13 oz); a newly hatched *A. f. bodini* 15 g ($\frac{1}{2}$ oz).
Immatures Duller head colour; rump and lower back mainly green; iris brown.
Origin Nominate race (illustrated above left) occurs in Brazil, Colombia and Peru, in the Amazon basin; Bodin's Amazon (*A. f. bodini*), illustrated above right, inhabits central Venezuela and north-western Guyana along the Orinoco, Casanare and Meta rivers.

Status Abundant because confined to river edges and seasonally flooded forest (varzea), which are undisturbed by human activity.
Aviculture Always uncommon; *A. f. bodini* virtually unknown until the 1980s; nominate race reared in perhaps only 2 collections because of lack of females.
Accommodation 8.
Diet 7.
Clutch size 3*.
Incubation 28 days*.
Young in nest Assume 8 weeks.

This is the only Amazon with lower back and rump red; it lacks red wing speculum. Its temperament is extremely excitable and most males are aggressive. It is an excellent mimic.

Yellow-faced Amazon   *Amazona xanthops*

German Gelbbauchamazone   **Dutch** Geelbuikamazone

Length 27 cm (10½ in).
Weight 260 g (9 oz) – up to 400 g (14 oz) in overweight birds; a newly hatched chick weighed 12 g (under ½ oz) (Silva, 1991).
Immatures Less extensive yellow on head; underparts green, or marked with yellow, or yellow and orange in the colourful phase; colour on head and abdomen increases with age.
Origin Brazil: interior of eastern and southern regions, eastern Bolivia and northernmost Paraguay.
Status Locally common in cerrado (lightly wooded grasslands), a habitat often destroyed for cattle grazing and therefore vulnerable.
Aviculture Almost unknown until late 1970s; remains rare; few breeding successes to date.
Accommodation 8.
Diet 7, with emphasis on fruits and vegetables as the bird is prone to obesity.
Clutch size 3.
Incubation 26 days.
Young in nest 8 weeks.

In behaviour, appearance and chromosome type, this is not a typical Amazon; further information may result in its being classified in another genus. It has 2 colour phases, 1 of which is sexually dimorphic, males having yellow and orange on abdomen (green in other phase).

Yellow-shouldered Amazon *Amazona barbadensis*

German Gelbschulteramazone   **Dutch** Geelschouderamazone

Length 31 cm (12 in).
Weight 270 g (9½ oz); newly hatched chicks weigh 10 g (⅓ oz).
Immatures Usually duller or less extensive head coloration; some individuals with blue on the forehead; iris brownish, changing to orange by 3 months.
Origin Venezuela, confined to a small coastal area; islands of Blanquilla and Margarita off the coast, and Bonaire (Netherlands Antilles).
Status Viable population in Venezuela, fluctuating population on Bonaire (drastic decline in drought period, Low, 1984); rapid decline during 1980s on Margarita due to destruction of habitat as a result of tourism; status on Blanquilla rare; on Appendix 1 of CITES.
Aviculture Rare but established due to gradually increasing breeding successes.
Accommodation 5 or 8 (aggressive nature of some males makes wing-clipping necessary, but not effective in small enclosure).
Diet 7.
Clutch size 3, more rarely 4.
Incubation About 26 days.
Young in nest 9 weeks.

Blue-fronted Amazon *Amazona aestiva*

German Blaustirnamazone   **Dutch** Blauwvoorhoofdamazone

Length 35 cm (14 in); *A. a. xanthopteryx* 37 cm (15 in).
Weight 375 g (13 oz) but up to 450 g (16 oz); *xanthopteryx* 400 g (14 oz) but up to 500 g (17½ oz).
Immatures Head colour variable but usually duller and less extensive and, in *xanthopteryx*, also less yellow on bend of wing.
Origin Nominate race occurs in Brazil, the inland eastern region as far south as southern Mato Grosso; *xanthopteryx* is found in southern Brazil (southern Mato Grosso), in Paraguay and northern Argentina.
Status Common in some areas but declining where extensive taking of young is occurring; during the period 1984–8, 82,000 (*xanthopteryx*) were imported into the USA.
Aviculture Always readily available and, since the 1980s, widely bred.
Accommodation 8.
Diet 7.
Clutch size 3 or 4.
Incubation 28 days.
Young in nest 8–9 weeks.

The sub-species *xanthopteryx* is illustrated; males have more yellow on the face than females. *A. a. aestiva* has bend of wing red or mainly red and is slightly smaller.

Yellow-fronted Amazon *Amazona ochrocephala ochrocephala*

German Gelbscheitelamazone (*A. o. ochrocephala*),
Panama-Amazone (*A. o. panamensis*)
Dutch Geelvoorhoofdamazone (*A. o. ochrocephala*),
Panama-amazone (*A. o. panamensis*)

Length 35 cm (14 in); *A. o. panamensis*, 31 cm (12 in).

Weight 380–480 g (13½–17 oz); newly hatched chicks weigh 12 g (about ½ oz).

Immatures Yellow on head less extensive and less well defined; beak and iris dark brown.

Origin Guianas, northern Brazil, northern Venezuela and Colombia in Norte de Santander and Meta; *A. o. panamensis* occurs from western Panama to northern Colombia (Magdalena to Santander in north-east and Chocó in the west).

Status Locally common in woodland.

Aviculture Nominate race is common, frequently bred; *A. o. panamensis* is uncommon.

Accommodation 8.

Diet 7.

Clutch size 3.

Incubation 26 days.

Young in nest About 9 weeks.

This is a very talented mimic and among the most popular Amazon as a pet. Nominate race illustrated above left, *A. o. panamensis* above right.

Double Yellow-headed Amazon *Amazona ochrocephala oratrix*

German Grosse Gelbkopfamazone   **Dutch** Dubbele geelkopamazone

Length 36–38 cm (14–15 in).
Weight 500 g (17½ oz); newly hatched chicks weigh 15 g (½ oz).
Immatures Yellow confined to forehead and crown; on fledging part of upper mandible dark grey; iris dark brown; full adult head colour is not acquired for 5 years or more.
Origin West coast of Mexico in Colima and Guerrero; *A. o. belizensis* is from Belize (British Honduras).
Status Declining due to habitat destruction and trade; *A. o. belizensis* has also declined.
Aviculture *A. o. oratrix* is common in the USA, fairly common elsewhere and frequently bred; *belizensis* is rarer (perhaps sometimes mistaken for immature *oratrix*).
Accommodation 8.
Diet 7.
Clutch size 2–4, usually 3.
Incubation 26 days.
Young in nest About 9 weeks.

This species is famed for its ability to mimic, both in speech and even 'song'. However, it can be extremely noisy.

Tres Marias Amazon *Amazona ochrocephala tresmariae*

German Tres-mariasamazone   **Dutch** Tres Mariasamazone

Information as for Double Yellow-headed Amazon (page 265) except:
Length 38 cm (15 in).
Weight 500 g (17½ oz).
Immatures More extensive yellow on head than other sub-species, extending over the side of the face; blue sheen on breast. In the sub-species *A. o. magna*, crown and cheeks only partially yellow.
Origin Tres Marias Islands, off west coast of Mexico; *A. o. magna* is from the Atlantic slope of Mexico from central Tamaulipas south to eastern Tabasco.

Status Locally common on Tres Marias.
Aviculture *A. o. magna* is fairly common in the USA, where it is almost invariably and incorrectly called 'Tres Marias Amazon'; elsewhere it is uncommon. Hansen (1991) summarizes the differences between the two sub-species, including the fact that *A. o. tresmariae* has blue sheen to underparts and lacks black margins to feathers of back and breast. Note that *A. o. magna* (illustrated above right) is much more colourful and *A. o. tresmariae* (illustrated above left) is much lighter yellow on the head.

Yellow-naped Amazon
Amazona ochrocephala auropalliata

German Gelbnackenamazone   **Dutch** Geelnekamazone

Length 35 cm (14 in).
Weight About 480 g (17 oz) but up to 550 g (19½ oz).
Immatures Little or no yellow on head and nape; beak grey but lower mandible horn-coloured in *A. o. parvipes*.
Origin Central America: Pacific slope from southern Mexico south through Guatemala and Nicaragua to Costa Rica; *A. o. parvipes* occurs in eastern-most Honduras and north-eastern Nicaragua (there is no official common name but Parvipes Amazon seems logical).

Status Common in some areas but endangered by habitat destruction in El Salvador.
Aviculture *A. o. auropalliata* (illustrated above left) is well known in the USA, rarer in Europe; *A. o. parvipes* has been known only since late 1970s; both races seldom bred.
Accommodation 8.
Diet 7.
Clutch size 2 or 3.
Incubation 26 days.
Young in nest 11 weeks.

Noisy and excitable, this species is aggressive when breeding. Yellow-naped is an exceptionally talented mimic. Note that only *A. o. parvipes* (illustrated above right) has red on bend of wing.

Orange-winged Amazon *Amazona amazonica*

German Venezuela–Amazone   **Dutch** Oranjevleugelamazone

Length 30–33 cm (12–13 in).
Weight 360 g (12½ oz) – up to 490 g (17½ oz) recorded.
Immatures Plumage like adult; iris greyish.
Origin South America, entire northern part east of Andes.
Status Common and widespread in lowlands.

Aviculture Always among the most common of the genus; fairly frequently bred; often kept as pet, despite unpleasant voice.
Accommodation 8.
Diet 7.
Clutch size 3 or 4.
Incubation 25 days.
Young in nest 8 weeks.

Mercenary Amazon *Amazona mercenaria*

German Soldatenamazone   **Dutch** Soldatenamazone

Length 43 cm (13 in).
Weight 300 g ($10\frac{1}{2}$ oz).
Immatures Undescribed; probably like adults with iris greyish.
Origin Mountains of western South America from Santa Marta in Colombia through the Andes south to northern Bolivia and Peru.

Status Uncommon, mainly between 1,500 m (5,000 ft) and 3,000 m (10,000 ft).
Aviculture Very rare; a few specimens imported into USA in 1983.
Accommodation 8.
Diet 7.

Nothing is known about its wild or captive reproduction.

Mealy Amazon   *Amazona farinosa*

German Mülleramazone   **Dutch** Mülleramazone

Length 38 cm (15 in).
Weight 540–700 g (19–25 oz)
Immatures Like adult or without yellow on forehead; iris brownish; dark tip to upper mandible on fledging.
Origin Ranges from southern Mexico through Central America (Caribbean slope) and most of northern South America to northern Bolivia and central-eastern Brazil; *A. f. guatemalae* is from southern Mexico (Oaxaca and Veracruz) southwards to Honduras.

Status Essentially a bird of continuous lowland forest, in some areas it is declining due to deforestation.
Aviculture Little known until late 1970s; rarely bred; does not nest readily.
Accommodation 5 or 8.
Diet 7.
Clutch size 3*.
Incubation 24–27 days recorded.
Young in nest 9–10 weeks.

With its 'gentle giant' temperament and its talent for mimicry, it would make an excellent pet were it not for its loud voice.

Kawall's Amazon *Amazona kawalli*

German Kawall's Amazone   **Dutch** Kawallamazone

Length 38 cm (15 in).
Weight 630 g (22½ oz) estimated.
Immatures Undescribed; probably like adult with iris brownish.
Origin Brazil, Amazonas region of the north-west.
Status Unknown.
Aviculture Unknown outside Brazil, where about 6 were known in 1988.

A single speciment was exhibited at London Zoo for at least 10 years from the early 1970s, labelled as a Mealy Amazon. Its superficial similarity to that species must be why it was for so long unrecognized. Assume avicultural information and breeding biology as for Mealy Amazon (opposite). This species was not officially described until 1989.

Vinaceous Amazon *Amazona vinacea*

German Taubenhalsamazone   **Dutch** Wijnborstamazone

Length 30 cm (12 in).
Weight 370 g (13 oz).
Immatures Duller red forehead, less vinous underparts; yellow on carpal edge of wing; iris brownish.
Origin Brazil, now known definitely only from southern Bahia, northern Espírito Santo and Rio Grande do Sul; south-eastern Paraguay and north-eastern Argentina.
Status Endangered; rapid decline and range contraction in past decade due to deforestation; populations in some areas estimated to have decreased from thousands to a few hundreds; on Appendix 1 of CITES.
Aviculture Uncommon; limited breeding.
Accommodation 8.
Diet 7.
Clutch size 3, occasionally 4.
Incubation 28 days*.
Young in nest About 9 weeks but 7 weeks recorded in a single instance.

This species deserves the attention of serious aviculturists.

Red-necked Amazon *Amazona arausiaca*

German Blaukopfamazone   **Dutch** Dominica-amazone

Length 39 cm (15½ in).
Weight 620 g (22½ oz) – 1 male only weighed.
Immatures Lack pink on throat (Evans, in prep., 1991); iris brownish or greyish.
Origin Dominica, Lesser Antilles, Caribbean; range now restricted to north of island.
Status Rare; latest estimate (May 1990) was of about 300 birds, but the number had increased and the range expanded during the previous 2 years (gradual recovery after Hurricanes David and Allen); on Appendix 1 of CITES.
Aviculture Always an extreme rarity; only 5 birds known outside Dominica at time of writing, including 1 pair in the USA; no captive breeding had occurred.
Accommodation 5.
Diet 7.
Clutch size 2*.
Incubation Probably 28 days.
Young in nest Probably 10–11 weeks.

St Vincent Amazon *Amazona guildingii*

German Königsamazone   **Dutch** St Vincentamazone

Length 41 cm (16 in).
Weight 580–700 g (21–25 oz).
Immatures Variable but usually duller, especially on head; upper mandible marked with grey and iris brown in newly fledged young.
Origin St Vincent (Lesser Antilles), Caribbean, in the central mountainous part of the island.
Status Endangered but fairly stable population, estimated as 440–500 in 1988; on Appendix 1 of CITES.
Aviculture Always rare; at the time of writing between 40 and 50 were known outside St Vincent, those responsible for them being members of an international consortium formed to breed this species (only 2 had succeeded and Ramon Noegel, Florida, had reared 11 by 1991).
Accommodation Walk-in or suspended aviary, minimum 4.5 m (15 ft) long.
Diet 7, with 70 per cent fruit and vegetables, sunflower limited to a few grains and fattening seeds reduced, since tendency to obesity.
Clutch size 2, rarely 3.
Incubation 25 or 26 days.
Young in nest 9–10 weeks.

There is more than one colour morph; in fact, most experts recognize three. They are orange to brown, brown (standard) and green (Noegel, 1990); the green morph is illustrated.